BEASTS AND SAINTS

BY HELEN WADDELL

———

PETER ABELARD
A Novel
16*th Printing*

THE WANDERING SCHOLARS
7*th Printing*

MEDIÆVAL LATIN LYRICS
4*th Printing*

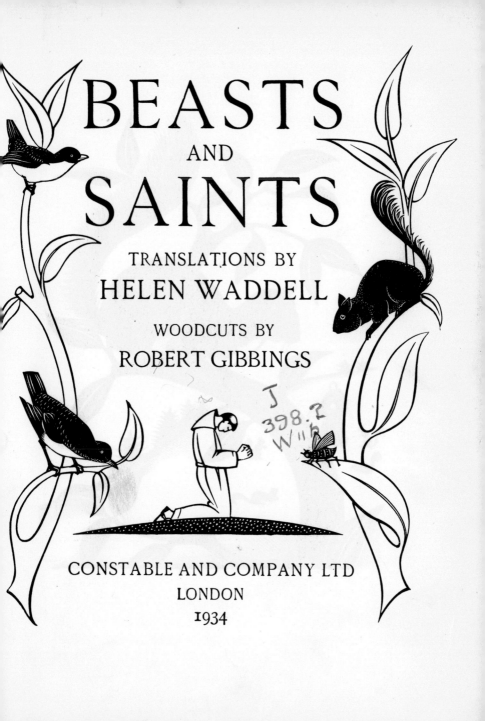

BEASTS
AND
SAINTS

TRANSLATIONS BY
HELEN WADDELL

WOODCUTS BY
ROBERT GIBBINGS

CONSTABLE AND COMPANY LTD
LONDON
1934

PUBLISHED BY

Constable and Company Ltd.

LONDON

·

Oxford University Press

BOMBAY CALCUTTA MADRAS

·

*The Macmillan Company
of Canada, Limited*

TORONTO

PRINTED IN GREAT BRITAIN.
CHISWICK PRESS: CHARLES WHITTINGHAM AND GRIGGS (PRINTERS), LTD.
NEW SOUTHGATE, LONDON, N.11.

CONTENTS

vii

3608   9

CONTENTS

THE SAINTS OF IRELAND

CONTENTS

TRANSLATOR'S NOTE

THESE are stories of the mutual charities between saints and beasts, from the end of the fourth to the end of the twelfth century. They are translated without sophistication from the original Latin, most of it of the same period : the detail of the actual sources will be found on the last pages of this book. By restricting these sources to Latin, I have had to forgo the race of the vernacular ; Robert Mannyng's bear who came to keep a lonely hermit in company, and as he came up to the gate louted and made fair cheer—" Feyre chere as a bere myght " : the four Irish scholars who went to sea for the love of God and took nothing with them, only that the youngest said, " I think I will take the little cat " : the grasshopper who came to Portiuncula through a winter's night to sing the midnight office for St. Francis, and left his small tracks in the snow, to the compunction of the slothful brethren who had lain warm in their beds. The truth is that the Middle Ages are so rich in this kind of story that without some arbitrary principle of selection one is hampered by too much liberty. Choice is difficult enough even in Latin, though here it has again been limited to the pre-Franciscan saints. St. Gerard's wolf that was bidden to impersonate the calf it had killed, and came and stood meekly before the distracted cow to her great satisfaction, till it wearied of this quiet life and suborned a young deer to take its place : St. Karilef's bison that came to him to be petted and scratched between its horns ; these and a score of good monsters have been omitted, together with the lions who dug a grave in the desert for Paul the Hermit, and who still weep wide-mouthed and dig on their capital at Vézelay, more movingly even than in St. Jerome's prose. But Jerome's *Vita Beati Pauli Eremitae* is too subtly constructed to be mutilated for the sake of a single episode, and must be translated in full in some other place.

St. Jerome indeed makes no appearance as author in this collection, though he shares the title-rôle with his Lion and his Donkey in its most considerable story; a story that throws an unusually mellow light on that scholarly and irascible saint. The manuscript that records it is not earlier than Xth-XIth century: there is the gravest suspicion that Jerome acquired his lion by confusion with St. Gerasimus, a less distinguished and more genial abbot a little higher up the Jordan, whose lion and donkey were a good deal less sophisticated than the animals of the later version. Erasmus spoke of it disdainfully as a fable unworthy the merits of so great a man, and even the grandmotherly benevolence of the *Patrologia* admits that it is without gravity, and pieced together *ab inepto sarcinatore*. Yet how the "inept botcher" enjoyed his tale, and his own preposterous prose: and how humane a figure is his *saepe praedictus pater*, his already frequently mentioned saint. *Hunc tamen ne exasperetis—* "Do not nag at him," said Jerome simply, when the brethren were blaming the lion on circumstantial evidence only. This is not the Jerome that Rufinus knew: but it is the Jerome that Carpaccio knew, and endeared to Christendom on the walls of San Giorgio di Schiavoni. Here is the benevolent old man who leads his lion into the cloister, while the affrighted monks swoop like swallows to their eaves; here is the lion that paces, affable and ingratiating, behind him: and here, impassive and self-sufficing to the last, is the donkey who crops the herbage in the cloister garth while Jerome dies in the foreground, and the lion rends heaven with his bootless cries.

It was Jerome's sometime friend Rufinus who is responsible for the story of the Blessed Ammon and the Dragons. It is from the *Historia Monachorum in Ægypto*, the tale of a journey undertaken by a party of seven persons to visit the monks and eremites of the *Thebaid* in the winter of the year 394. It is not certain that he was one of the party : but the book was either written or translated by him for the brethren of his monastery on the Mount of Olives. He was given to grunting a little in his speech, so that Jerome unkindly called him Grunnius : lavishly hospitable, a trifle luxurious in his tastes, and a hearty admirer of asceticism in others. A similar account, the *Historia Lausiaca*, was written in Greek by Palladius, a friendly, inquisitive, and much journeying monk, who held St. Jerome's scholarship and venom in equal awe, but was a staunch disciple and lover of St. John Chrysostom. His experience of the desert stretched over the last ten years of the century, but the book was not written till 420, when the wanderer had become a bishop. His story of St. Macarius and the Hyæna is the only extract taken not from the Latin, but from the infinitely more spirited Coptic version translated by Amélineau.

Most of the stories of the Desert Fathers were translated into Latin from their original Greek, during the fifth, sixth and seventh centuries. St. Pachome who summoned crocodiles to ferry him as one calls a cab from a rank, died, a very old man, about 405, and his life was translated in the sixth century by the abbot Dionysius Exiguus, so called not because he was a little man, but because of his great humbleness. St. Simeon Stylites, himself the most dragonish of the Saints, converted his dragon sixteen years before his death in 460 ; his life was written by

xiii

Antonius his disciple. The story of the Unsociable Lion, a
very rare instance of grudging hospitality, comes from the
Verba Seniorum, translated by John the Subdeacon, pos-
sibly he who succeeded Pelagius in St. Peter's chair in
599 ; while the story of Gerasimus and the Lion is from
the *Pratum Spirituale*, written by John Moschus, himself
familiar with the desert, about 620.

Yet the most fragrant of these stories, *The Hermit's
Garden* and *The Penitent Wolf*, are from a Latin original.
They were told to Sulpicius Severus by his friend
Postumianus, just off his ship at Narbonne, after three years
journeying in North Africa : the two sat together on their
cloaks, Postumianus now and then hitching his a little
nearer. The *Dialogus* which records that conversation is
one of the earliest instances of the idiosyncrasy of French
prose, although the words are Latin : and the pages of it
are haunted by a gracious ghost, the Abbé Brémond of
blessed memory, so near a neighbour in birthplace though
so far divided in time, and master, like his predecessor,
of a gay and gentle irony. Sulpicius was a barrister of
Toulouse, friend and contemporary of St. Paulinus of
Nola : like him, he was fortunate in birth and ambition
and friendship : and like him, renounced the world in his
prime. But a kind of exquisite worldliness kept with him,
a sidelong glancing wit, and a way of writing prose that
runs like water. The *Dialogues* were probably written about
405, a few years before Sulpicius died in 410, the year of
the sack of Rome. His friend Paulinus survived him, and
Rome, for another twenty years.

Of the Saints of the West, *The Death of King Teudiric*
belongs to that century and country about the Severn Sea,
which is the matrix of the legend of Arthur and the last
fight with heathendom. It is embedded in the *Book of Llan
Dâv*, among charters and boundaries, its purpose there

being to explain the possession by the bishops of Llandaff of the lands about Mathern, free of tax or impost to any secular man, inasmuch as Mouric gave the earth upon which his father died to St. Oudouceus, Bishop of Llandaff, and his successors in the see, for ever. St. Oudouceus died early in the seventh century : the book was compiled in the twelfth : but the story, like its more famous counterpart, has the quality of timelessness.

The next two legends, *St. Columba and the Crane*, *St. Columba and the White Horse*, are rooted in a craggier soil : they are the gentlest things recorded of the heroic and tempestuous abbot who founded Iona. The *regio nostrae paternitatis*, the countryside where he and his crane alike were fathered, is Gartan in Donegal, at the ingoing of the mountains and the great lake ; a gentle countryside, and more apt a birthplace for the bird that came flying, buffeted with wind, and fell exhausted on the western beach, than for that other precipitous spirit. The life, written about 690 by Adamnan, also an Irishman, and himself abbot of Iona, is a rugged piece of work : but the death-days of the Saint, and the crowding torches that discovered him dying in the dark before the high altar at midnight of the 9th of June, are one of the tidemarks in medieval prose.

The life of Columbanus, " Prince of Druids," founder of Luxeuil and Bobbio and a Rule of passionate austerity, was written by Jonas, a monk of his own abbey of Bobbio, some time after 640 : Columban himself died in 615. St. Malo, the saint of Brittany, died three years after him : his life was written five centuries later by a quiet scholar, Sigebert of Gembloux, about whom, said his admiring disciple, there was always an air " of antique knowledge and reverence." The stories of St. Cuthbert are from the life by the Venerable Bede : they show in little the quality

not only of the saint of the Farnes but of his biographer :
the historian's care to note source and authority : the
quick eye that had observed how a horse crops and pulls
at the hay above its head, and how a sad bird trails its
wings : and an even narrative prose that can deepen to a
solemnity that is, in his own phrase, *undisonus*, its sound
like the sea.

St. Werburga and the Wild Geese, on the other hand, is
William of Malmesbury in his voice of cheerful gossip,
narrating a local miracle : the abbess died about the year
700. Benno, Bishop of Meissen, was a spirited saint (he
died at a great age in 1106) who took the precaution, before
obeying a summons to Rome, of bidding two trusty canons
lock his cathedral doors in case of trouble and throw the
keys into the Elbe : whence they were recovered, under the
fin of an obliging fish, upon its astute bishop's return.
His life was written in 1512 by Jerome Emser, a Doctor
of Canon Law, author of a dialogue as to whether potation
is to be tolerated in a properly constituted State, and of
tracts against the more spiritual intemperances of Luther
and Zwingli. One observes the agreeable Renaissance
pedantry with which the over-loquacious frog is bidden
to be a Seraphian, inasmuch as the frogs in the island of
Seraphus are mute, and can but admire the ease with which
the frog, knowing his Pliny, was able to take the allusion.
St. Godric of Finchale is with Bartholomew of Farne
(*ob.* c. 1193), the most recent of the saints : he died about
1170, at a great age. He was a Norfolk man, a pedlar, and
then took to sea and became a ship's captain : he may be
the *Gudericus pirata* who carried Baldwin to Jaffa in 1102 :
at any rate, though he died far inland, he would to the end
of his days be troubled on stormy nights for ships at sea.
He was a pilgrim to the Holy Sepulchre : and coming out
of the waters of the Jordan, and looking down at his feet,

xvi

" ' Lord,' said he within himself, ' for love of Thy name, Who for men's salvation didst walk always barefoot through the world, and didst not deny to have Thy naked feet struck through with nails for me : from this day I shall put no shoes upon these feet.' " It is the accent of the liturgy, the poetry of plain men. He kept his vow to the end : and his biographer and younger contemporary, Reginald of Durham, knew him go barefoot through the frost, peering under hedges for such small animals as might be helpless with the cold.

The last section, The Saints in Ireland, derives from the collection of saints' lives in various Trinity and Rawlinson MSS. edited by Plummer in the *Vitae Sanctorum Hiberniae*. The story of St. Kevin and the Blackbird is from Giraldus Cambrensis : the Fly who would keep his place in the codex for St. Colman is from Colgan's pleasant seventeenth-century prose, retelling in Latin the legends which " Ketinus " (Joseph Keating) had already collected in Irish. The others are probably the work of Irish monks as late as the twelfth century, yet they are in some sort the most archaic of all, both in the simplicity of the narration and the untroubled acceptance of the ancient understanding, that one finds in folklore, between man and beast.

" Here one would take
A fox and one a deer for acolyte,
And fresh from night
The hawthorn brake
With you gave thanks in scent and song for light."[1]

Except Ciaran of Saigir, who is made contemporary with St. Patrick, the saints belong to the sixth and seventh

[1] Robin Flower : *Peregrinari pro amore Dei* in " Poems and Translations " (1931).

xvii

centuries. St. Ciaran, founder of Clonmacnoise where the kings are buried,

" Battle-banners of the Gael, that in Kiaran's plain of crosses
Their final hosting keep,"

died in 549 : St. Brendan of the Voyages in 577 : St. Cainnic, abbot of Aghaboe, in 599 : St. Colman mac Duach in 611 : St. Kevin (Coemgann) of Glendalough in 618 : St. Moling of Ferns in 697.

" Marvellous "—it is Colgan's meditation on the good offices of St. Colman's fly—" are these condescensions of the grace of God . . . yet how befitting His loving-kindness that those who have renounced all fellowship and service of men . . . should themselves receive the good offices of dumb beasts and a kind of human ministering." Yet the Saints have had no monopoly of the kindness that is between men and beasts. Homer pitied the crying of the sea-birds when the village folk have stolen their unfledged young from the nest : and old Argos on the dunghill, full of fleas, wagging his tail and dropping his ears at the sound of Odysseus' voice, but unable to drag himself nearer for old age, is the most moving thing of its kind in literature. Plutarch was eloquent on the " native magnanimity " that he found more often in beasts than in mankind : and he is never so engaging as when he describes the elephant that knew itself more stupid than the rest of the troupe, and was found one night rehearsing and " conning its lessons " by moonlight ; or the hedgehog who goes through a vineyard laboriously impaling grapes upon its little spines, till finally, itself a walking bunch of grapes, it bends its steps towards home and the regaling of its family : or the horn-owl who so admires the rhythmic dancing of men that it watches them in an ecstasy, humping its shoulders and jigging on its perch, and lo, the fowler creeps up behind and takes him unawares. It is a hard heart that will not lament him, or that will not contrast " the lovely friendship and civil society of pismires " with that of politicians. Boethius, himself in prison, wrote half a dozen lines on a wild bird caged in a cellar that sprang too high and saw the waving trees, and how thereafter it spurned its seed and its honeyed drink with small indignant claws.

" And all day long it pines for the green leaves,
And whispering ' the woods ', it grieves—it grieves."

Twelve centuries later Swift opened his cupboard door to put coal on the fire, after Patrick was gone to bed ; " and there I saw in a closet a poor linnet he has bought to bring over to Dingley. . . . I believe he does not know he is a bird : where you put him, there he stands, and seems to have neither hope nor fear." St. Malo would not move his cloak, because a wren had nested in it : and the other day a professional in a golf championship let go his chance of it, because he would not play his ball out of a thrush's nest.

For if the dark places of the earth have always been full of the habitations of cruelty, there has always been a spring of mercy in mankind. The Roman virtue of *pietas* is the strong root from which our pity, in every sense, derives. Religion has had its own savageries: yet even the arbitrary Godhead of the Book of Job was concerned for the young ravens wandering from the nest for lack of meat, and it was Christ's claim that a huddle of feathers on the ground was not unregarded by the Father of mankind. " With Christ," said Sulpicius Severus, " every brute beast is wise, and every savage creature gentle ": and St. Kevin refused the levelling of the mountains about Glendalough to make his monks rich pasture, because he would

not have God's creatures disturbed for him. In the first
paradise that lies behind the memory of the world there
was no cruelty: and when Isaiah, sick of war, made his
poem of the golden world, the climax-vision was a holy
mountain where " they shall not hurt nor destroy." And
whether these ancient ways of thought seem to us only the
delusions sloughed by a wiser world, or whether

> " those first affections,
> Those shadowy recollections . . .
> Are still the fountain-light of all our day.
> Are still a master-light of all our seeing "

it matters very little.

> " For still the heart doth need a language, still
> Doth the old instinct bring back the old names."

The beasts have still their way with us: Dürer's hare looks
out on the world with his timid confiding; and the gentlest
of the gods still has in his armoury

> " a twilight air
> That can make anchorites of kings."

THE DESERT FATHERS

THE HERMIT'S GARDEN IN THE DESERT

WHEN I first entered the desert, about twelve miles from the Nile —I had one of the brethren for guide, a man who knew the country well— we came to where an old monk lived at the foot of a mountain. And there, a thing very rare in those parts, was a well. He had an ox, whose sole business it was to draw up the water by turning a wheel : for the well was said to be a thousand or more feet deep. He had a garden too, full of many sorts of vegetables : a thing against nature in the desert, where everything is so parched and burnt by the rays of the sun that it seldom gives root or seed, and then but scant. But the labour that the saint shared with his ox, and his own industry, were to profit: for the constant watering gave such richness to the sand that we saw the herbs growing in the garden, green and lavish. On these the ox lived, together with his master : and from this plenty the good man provided a feast for us as well. I saw then what you

men of Gaul will hardly believe, the pot
of vegetables that he was preparing for our
meal boiling without any fire under it : so
great is the heat of the sun that it would
cook a Gallic meal as well as any cooks you
please.

After supper, as evening drew on, he
invited us to a palm tree, the fruit of which
he sometimes used ; it was about two miles
away. For these trees indeed exist in the
desert, though not many : and whether it
was the skill of the men of old time, or the
nature of the soil, begat them, I know not :
or else God foreseeing that the desert would
some day be inhabited by the saints, prepared them for His servants. For the most
part, those who live in these remote solitudes
live on the fruit of these trees, since no other
succeeds in growing here.

We came then to this tree, led by our
kindly host : and there stumbled upon a
lion. At sight of him, my guide and I quaked,
but the saintly old man went unfalteringly
on, and we followed him, timorously enough.
The wild beast—you would say it was at
the command of God—modestly withdrew a
little way and sat down, while the old man

4

plucked the fruit from the lower branches.
He held out his hand, full of dates; and up
the creature ran and took them as frankly
as any tame animal about the house : and
when it had finished eating, it went away.
We stood, watching and trembling ; reflect-
ing, as well we might, what valour of faith
was in him, and what poverty of spirit in us.

THE PENITENT WOLF

ANOTHER man, no less remarkable, we saw, living in a poor hut, where only one could enter at a time. The story was told of him that a she-wolf used to stand beside him at his meal, and that never did the creature fail to come at the appointed time, or to wait outside until he offered her whatever bread had been left over from his poor meal : and then she would lick his hand, and as if her task were over and the comfort of her presence duly given, would go away.

But it once so happened that the holy man had gone with a brother who had come to see him, to put him on his way, and was a long time absent, not getting home until nightfall. Meantime the beast had come at the usual meal hour. She felt that her friend and patron was absent, and went into his empty cell, inquisitive to find where its inhabitant might be. By chance a palm-basket with five loaves was hanging within reach : she ventured to take one, devoured it, and then, the crime perpetrated, made off.

The hermit came in, and saw his basket torn: he perceived the damage his household store had suffered, and near the threshold he recognized the crumbs where someone had been eating bread : nor had he much doubt as to the person of the thief. Then as the days went by and the creature did not come—too conscious of her bold act to come to him she had wronged, and affect innocence—the hermit took it sorely to heart that he had lost the company of his pet. At last when the seventh day had gone by, his prayers were answered : there she was, as he sat at his meal, as of old. But it was easy to perceive the embarrassment of the penitent : she stood, not daring to come near, her eyes fixed in profound shame upon the ground, and plainly entreating pardon. Pitying her confusion, the hermit called her to come near, and with a caressing hand he stroked the sad head : and finally, refreshed his penitent with two loaves for one. And she, forgiveness won and her grieving ended, resumed her wonted office. Consider, I pray you, in this example of it the power of Christ, with whom every brute beast is wise, and every savage creature gentle.

7

THE BLESSED AMMON AND
THE DRAGONS

SO then, we had taken leave of the blessed Apollonius and were journeying to the parts of the desert over against the south, when we saw in the sand the marks of the trail of a huge dragon : it was as if a beam had been dragged over the sand, so vast did it appear to be. At the sight of it, we were terror-stricken. But the brethren who were our guides exhorted us to be in no fear whatever, but rather to have faith and follow the dragon's tracks. " For you shall see," said they, " what faith can do, when you behold him extinguished by us. Many a dragon and serpent and horned beast have we slain with our hands, even as it is written that the Lord gave them that believed in Him power to tread upon serpents and scorpions and over all the power of the enemy." But even as they spoke, the frailty of our unbelief made us quake more and more, and we begged them not to follow the tracks of the dragon, but keep to our own straight course. One of them,

8

however, in the keenness of his spirit,
would himself go after the dragon : and
finding her cave not far off, shouted at us
to come over to him, and we should see
what befell.

At this point, however, a brother who
lived in the desert close by, came up to us
and forbade us to follow the dragon, declaring that we could not endure the sight of her,
especially as we were not in the habit of
seeing the like : he said that he himself had
often seen this very beast : that she was of
incredible bulk, and fifteen cubits in length.
And after urging us to go to his own house,
he himself hurried off to bring away the
brother, who was standing waiting for us
yonder, all in trim for the slaying of the
beast, and made him come back with him,
reluctant as he was to leave without destroying her: he had much ado to turn him
from his purpose. And when he had come up
with us, he had many hard words for our
poor-spiritedness and lack of faith.

So, arrived at our friend's cell, we sat
down to rest, and had no small kindness
from him. He told us that in this place
where he himself was living, there had

9

dwelt a holy man whose disciple he himself had been : his name was Ammon ; and the Lord had done mighty wonders through him. And among others, he told us this tale.

Often, he said, thieves would come to him and steal his bread, which was all he lived on, and whatever of his meagre store he might have laid aside. Again and again he suffered this molestation from them : till one day he set out into the desert and led home with him two enormous dragons to be in attendance on him, instructing them to stay by his monastery gate, and guard the entrance. Up came the thieves as usual, not knowing what custodians were now posted at the threshold: and at sight of the dragons, their wits and their strength went from them, and they fell speechless to the ground. And when the old man was aware, he came out, found them half dead, and picking them up, scolded them, saying, " See now how much hardier you be than the beasts : for these obey me for God's sake, whereas ye not only have no fear of God, but think it no shame to harry His servants." Nevertheless he brought them into his cell, set a table before them and bade them eat. And they, touched to the heart and all their inhumanity abandoned, in a short while became better men than many who had begun to serve God long before them. . . .

Another time it befell that a most brutal dragon was laying waste the countryside and slaughtering many : and the country folk came to this Father, begging him to rid the place of this beast. At the same time, to rouse the old man's pity, they carried with them a lad, a shepherd's son, who had been struck to the ground in terror at the mere sight of the dragon, and was left lifeless and swollen from the creature's breath. He anointed the lad with oil, and made him well again. But meantime, although inwardly he was spurring himself to the slaying of the dragon, he would promise them nothing, making as though he could be of no help to them.

Next morning he was up early, and on his way to the dragon's retreat : and there, setting his knees upon the ground, he entreated the Lord. Then the beast with a mighty rush came out upon him, breathing black foul fumes and uttering hisses and shrill shrieks. But he, in no way perturbed, turned towards the dragon and said, "May

11

Christ the Son of God slay thee, even as He shall slay the great whale." And at the old man's word, that most dire dragon vomited forth its spirit and its venom together, and burst asunder with a loud crack. And all the dwellers in that countryside came up and stood dumb at so mighty a miracle : and unable to bear the vehement stench, they heaped on him vast mounds of sand, while Father Ammon still stood by : for even though the creature were dead, they dared not come near it unless he were by.

12

ST. MACARIUS OF ALEXANDRIA AND THE GRATEFUL HYÆNA

IT happened one day as he was sitting in his cell, a hyæna came to him, her whelp was in her mouth; she set it down beside the door, she knocked on the door with her head. The old man heard her knock, he came out thinking that a brother had come to him. When he opened the door he saw the hyæna, he was astounded, saying, "What does she want here?" She filled her mouth with her whelp, she held it out to the old man, weeping. The old man took the whelp in his hands, steady in simplicity, he turned it this way and that, looking in its body for what ailed it. When he had considered the whelp, behold, it was blind in its two eyes. He took it, he groaned, he spat on its face, he signed it on the eyes with his finger : straightway the whelp saw, it went to its mother's dug, it sucked, it followed her, they went away to that river . . . and into the marsh they made their way. The sheep of the Lybians, they bring them once each year into the marsh of Scete to eat the *shoushet,* and the herdsmen that live in the villages over against

Pernouj, they also bring their oxen into the
marsh of Scete to eat the green herbage, once
a year.

The hyæna left a day behind her. The next
day she came to the old man, she had a sheepskin in her mouth, thick with wool, freshly
killed, she had it over her ; she struck the door
with her head. The old man was sitting in the
enclosure. When he heard the knock at the
door, he got up, he opened it : he found the
hyæna, the sheepskin over her. He said to the
hyæna, " Where hast thou been ? Where hast
thou found this, if thou hast not eaten a sheep?
As that which thou hast brought me comes of
violence, I will not take it."

The hyæna struck her head upon the ground,
she bent her paws, and on her knees she prayed
him, as if she had been a man, to take it. He
said to her, " I have but now told thee that I
will not take it, unless thou makest me this
promise : *I will not vex the poor by eating their
sheep.*" She made many movements of her
head, up and down, as if she were promising
him. Again he repeated it to her, saying,
" Unless thou dost promise me, saying, *I will
not kill a creature alive* ; but from to-day thou
wilt eat thy prey when it is dead. If thou art

14

distressed, seeking and finding none, come hither, and I will give thee bread. From this hour, do hurt to no creature." And the hyæna bowed her head to the ground, and dropped on her knees, bending her paws, moving her head up and down, looking at his face as if she were promising him. And the old man perceived in his heart that it was the purpose of God who gives understanding to beasts for a reproach unto ourselves, and he gave glory to God who gives understanding to the beasts, he sang in the Egyptian tongue God who liveth for ever, for the soul hath honour: he said, "I give glory to Thee, O God, who wast with Daniel in the lion's den, who didst give understanding unto beasts: also Thou hast given understanding to this hyæna and Thou hast not forgotten me : but Thou hast made me perceive that it is Thy ordering." And the old man took the skin from the hyæna, and she went away. From time to time she would come to seek the old man ; if she had not been able to find food, she would come to him and he would throw her a loaf. She did this many a time. And the old man slept on the skin until he died. And I have seen it with my own eyes.

ST. PACHOME, ABBOT OF TABENNE, AND THE CROCODILES

AT another time the cohorts of the devils plotted to tempt the man of God by a certain phantasy. For a crowd of them assembling together, were seen by him tying up the leaf of a tree with great ropes and tugging it along with immense exertion, ranked in order on the right and the left : and the one side would exhort the other, and strain and tug, as if they were moving a stone of enormous weight. And this the wicked spirits were doing so as to move him, if they could, to loud laughter, and so they might cast it in his teeth. But Pachome, seeing their impudence, groaned, and fled to the Lord with his accustomed prayers : and straightway by the virtue of Christ all their triangular array was brought to naught. . . .

After this, so much trust had the blessed Pachome learned to place in God . . . that many a time he trod on snakes and scorpions, and passed unhurt through all : and the crocodiles, if ever he had necessity to cross the river, would carry him with the utmost subservience, and set him down at whatever spot he indicated.

THE ABBOT HELENUS AND THE
WILD ASS

AT one time he was on his way to visit certain brethren who were ill, and carrying with him such things as the comfort of their bodies required. But as he walked, the heavy load that he carried began to distress him ; and seeing some distance off a herd of wild asses crossing the desert, he cried out to them, saying, " In the name of our Lord Jesus Christ, let one of you come here and take my pack." And lo, one out of the whole herd made its way to him, in all gentleness. And so he set his load on the willing creature, and himself as well, and was carried with all swiftness to the cells of the brethren whither he was journeying.

THE ABBOT HELENUS AND THE CROCODILE

HE came at one time upon certain monks, upon a Sabbath day, and said to them, "Why are ye not at Mass?" They made plain reply, "Because the priest has not come." Then said he, "I shall go and call him." Then they said that no one could cross the river, because of the depth of its channel. Also they said that there was a great beast in that place, namely a crocodile, who had eaten many men.

He, nevertheless, made no tarrying, but straightway getting up, made his way to the ford : and the crocodile at once took him upon its back and ferried him over to the opposite bank. He found the priest in the fields, and prayed him not to neglect the brotherhood. The priest, seeing him hung about with many patched rags, asked him where he got his coat, saying, "Thou hast a most fair garment for thy soul, my brother," and marvelling at his humility and frugality, followed him on his way to

the river. And when they could find no
skiff to ferry them across, the Abbot
Helenus sent out a shout, to summon the
crocodile. She at once obediently came
up, and flattened her back : the Abbot
invited the priest to mount along with him :
but he, stricken with alarm at sight of the
crocodile, retraced his steps. And great
was his admiration, and that of the brethren
on the further bank, when they saw the
Abbot crossing the river upon a crocodile.
Climbing up the bank, he drew the crocodile
after him, saying, " Better is it for her that
she should die, than suffer the penalty for
the slaughter of souls." And the crocodile
fell down, and died on the spot.

ST. SIMEON STYLITES AND THE CONVERTED DRAGON

THE fame of the holy man increased throughout the world, and they built him a pillar twelve cubits high, and he stood upon it twelve years. And again they built him a pillar twenty cubits high, and he stood upon it twelve years. Then all that dwelt in that place came together, and they built two churches beside the pillar, and a pillar thirty cubits high, and he stood upon it four years, and began to do miracles. . . . And many people he turned to the Christian faith, namely Saracens and Persians and Armenians and Laotians and the Foreigners. . . .

And after these days they again built him a pillar forty cubits high, and he stood upon it for sixteen years until his death. Now at that time there was an exceeding large dragon that lived close by, in the country to the north : and because of him no grass ever grew there : and a branch of a tree fell into his right eye. And lo, one day the blind dragon came, dragging himself along, and he applied himself to the pillar which was the habitation of the man of God, and winding himself into a wheel as if to ask pardon, lay with his head bowed low. And the blessed Simeon gazed down upon him, and straightway, the branch fell out of his eye : and it was a cubit in length. And indeed all that saw it glorified God, notwithstanding that they fled from him in terror. But the creature coiled itself up and stayed quiet in one place, whilst all the people went by. Then rising up, it worshipped at the gate of the monastery for wellnigh two hours, and so returned to its den, and did no hurt to any.

THE UNSOCIABLE LION

THERE was a certain old man, a solitary, who lived near the river Jordan: and going into a cave because of the heat, he found there a lion : and the lion began to gnash his teeth and to roar. To whom the old man said, " What is annoying thee? There is room enough here to hold both me and thee. And if thou likest it not, arise and go hence." But the lion, not taking it well, left and went outside.

THE ABBOT GERASIMUS AND
THE LION

ABOUT a mile distant from the Jordan is
a monastery, called after the Abbot
Gerasimus. On our coming to the
monastery the old men who dwelt there told
us of the Abbot Gerasimus, how one day
walking on the banks of the Jordan he met a
lion making a mighty roaring, and one paw
dangling: and sticking in the paw was the
sharp point of a reed, so that the paw was
swollen and full of matter. When the lion saw
the old man, it showed him the paw with the
thorn fixed in it, weeping after its fashion and
beseeching him to have some care of it. And
the old man seeing him in such sore straits,
sat down and took the paw, opened it and
drew out the thorn with a great deal of pus,
cleansed the wound carefully, bound it up
with a rag, and sent him away. But the lion
finding himself cured would not leave the old
man, but followed after him wherever he went
as a dear disciple his master, so that the old
man marvelled at the gratitude of a wild
beast. And thenceforward the old man would

feed him, setting bread before him and soaked herbs.

Now the monastery had a donkey to draw water from the Jordan for the brethren's needs. And the old man made it a rule that the lion should take charge of the donkey. And so he would go off with him along the banks of the Jordan, and watch him grazing. But one day while the donkey was browsing the lion had gone some little distance away; and lo! a camel driver from Arabia came upon the donkey and took him and led him away. The lion, his donkey lost, returned sorely dejected to the monastery, and came with drooping head and neck before his abbot. Now the Abbot Gerasimus thought that he had devoured the donkey, and said, "Where is the donkey?" He stood silent and downcast, like any man. Then said the old man, "Thou hast eaten him: blessed be God. Whatsoever the ass did, from this time forward thou shalt do." After which, at the old man's bidding, the lion wore panniers that held four jars, and carried the water for the monastery.

Now one day a certain soldier came to the old man for his blessing, and when he saw the lion carrying his burden and learned the reason, he was sorry for him, and offered three pieces of money to the old men to buy a donkey for this business of water-carrying, and release the lion from that necessity. A little while had gone by after his deliverance from this task, when the camel driver who had stolen the donkey was coming with barley to sell it in the Holy City, and the donkey with him. He had crossed the Jordan where he came upon the lion: and at sight of him he left his camels and fled. The lion, recognizing the donkey, ran up to him, and holding the halter in his mouth as he was wont, drew him along with the three camels, and jubilant and roaring at finding his lost donkey, came to the old man. The old man who had originally thought that the lion had eaten the donkey now perceived that he had been taken unawares. And he called the lion Jordanes. And for more than five years the lion went about among the brethren in the monastery, never quitting the old man.

But when the Abbot Gerasimus passed over to the Lord, and was buried by the fathers, it befel, by the dispensation of God, that the lion was not to be found. After a little while he comes in, and begins looking for his old

27

master. The Abbot Sabbatius Cilix, who had been disciple to the Abbot Gerasimus, saw him and said, " Jordanes, our old master has left us orphans, and has passed over to the Lord: yet take and eat." But the lion would not eat, but went ceaselessly here and there, turning about and looking round to see his old master, and signifying by a mighty roaring that he could not bear him to be absent. The Abbot Sabbatius and the other old men would ruffle his head and say to him, " The old master has gone to God and left us." But nothing they said could appease his roaring and lamenting: for the more they tried to caress and console him the more he grieved and the louder he roared, adding lament upon lament, and showing in voice and visage and eye the grief that he was in at not seeing the old man.

Then the Abbot Sabbatius said to him, " Come with me, since you will not believe us, and I will show you where our old master is laid." And he took him and led him to where they had buried him. It was about five paces from the church. And the Abbot Sabbatius, standing by the grave of the Abbot Gerasimus, said to the lion, " Look: our old master is buried here.'' And the Abbot Sabbatius bowed his knees beside the old man's grave. And when the lion heard it and saw the Abbot Sabbatius prone upon the grave and weeping, he laid himself down, beating his head upon the earth and roaring: and he died there, on the old man's grave.

ST. JEROME AND THE LION AND THE DONKEY

IMPOSSIBLE and long it would be to unfold all that might be told of that great man and his austere life and ways. Yet one miracle about this monastery there is, like those of old time, that oblivion hath not yet stolen from memory, for it is handed down from one to another, and told by holy men that lived in Bethlehem for love of the heavenly fatherland: and it I now weave into this compendious discourse.

Upon a certain day as evening drew on, and the blessed Jerome sat with the brethren, as is the way of the monk, to hear the reading of the lesson and to speak good words, lo of a sudden, limping on three paws and the fourth caught up, came a mighty lion into the cloister. At sight of him a good many of the brethren fled in terror, for human frailty is but timorous. But the blessed Jerome went out to meet him as one greets an incoming guest.

And while the distance between them was shortening, the lion who had no way of speaking, it not being his nature, offered the good father as best he might his wounded paw: and the Saint, calling the brethren, gave instructions that the wounded paw should be bathed, to find why the lion went thus limping. Upon close examination, they found that the paw had been pierced by thorns. Fomentations were applied with all diligence, and the wound speedily healed.

And now, all wildness and savagery laid aside, the lion began to go to and fro among them as peaceable and domestic as any animal about the house. This the blessed Jerome observed, and spoke as follows to the brethren: "Bring your minds to bear upon this, my brethren: what, I ask you, can we find for this lion to do in the way of useful and suitable work, that will not be burdensome to him, and that he can efficiently accomplish? For I believe of a surety that it was not so much for the healing of his paw that God sent him hither, since He could have cured him without us, as to show us that He is anxious to provide marvellous well for our necessity."

To which the brethren gave concerted and humble response: "Thou knowest, father, that the donkey who brings us our wood from the forest pasture needs some one to look after him, and that we are always in fear that some naughty beast will devour him. Wherefore if it seem to thee good and right, let the charge of our donkey be laid upon the lion, that he may take him out to pasture, and again may bring him home."

And so it was done: the donkey was put in charge of the lion, as his shepherd: together they took the road to the pasture, and wherever the donkey grazed, there was his defender: and a sure defence he was. Nevertheless, at regular hours, that he might refresh himself and the donkey do his appointed task, the lion would come with him home.

And so for long enough it was: till one day, the donkey duly brought to his pasture, the lion felt a great weight of sluggishness come upon him, and he fell asleep. And as he lay sunk in deep slumber, it befell that certain merchants came along that road on their way to Egypt to buy oil. They saw the donkey grazing, they saw that no guardian was at hand, and seized by sudden wicked greed, they caught him and led him away.

In due course the lion roused up, knowing nothing of his loss, and set out to fetch his charge at graze. But when he was not to be seen in the accustomed pasture, constricted with anxiety and in deep distress the lion went roaring up and down, hither and thither, for the remainder of the day, seeking what he had lost. And at last, when all hope of finding the donkey was gone, he came and stood at the monastery gate.

Conscious of guilt, he no longer dared walk in as of old time with his donkey. The blessed Jerome saw him, and the brethren too, hanging about outside the gate, without the donkey, and long past his usual hour: and they concluded that he had been tempted by hunger to kill his animal. In no mind, therefore, to offer him his wonted ration, " Away with you," said they, " and finish up whatever you have left of the donkey, and fill your greedy belly." And yet even as they spoke, they were doubtful as to whether he had indeed perpetrated this crime or no.

So finally the brethren went out to the pasture whither the lion was wont to bring the animal aforesaid, and up and down they scoured, to see if they could find any trace of the slaughter. No sign of violence was to be seen: and turning home they made haste to

D

bring their report to the blessed Jerome. He heard them, and spoke. " I entreat you, brethren," said he, " that although ye have suffered the loss of the ass, do not, nevertheless, nag at him or make him wretched. Treat him as before, and offer him his food: and let him take the donkey's place, and make a light harness for him so that he can drag home the branches that have fallen in the wood." And it was done.

So the lion did regularly his appointed task, while the time drew on for the merchants to return. Then one day, his work done, he went out, inspired as I believe, brute beast though he was, by some divine prompting, and made his way to the field. Up and down, hither and thither in circles he ran, craving some further light on the fate that had befallen his comrade. And finally, worn out but still anxious, he climbed to a rising above the highway where he might look all round him. A great way off he spied men coming with laden camels, and in front of them walked a donkey. So far off was he that he could not recognize him. None the less he set out, stepping cautiously, to meet them.

Now it is said to be the custom in that part

of the country that whenever men set out with camels on a long journey, a donkey goes in front, with the camel's halter on its neck, and the camels follow after. And now the merchants came nearer, and he recognized his donkey. With a fierce roar he charged down upon them, making a mighty din, though doing no damage to any. Crazed with terror, as they well might be, they left all they had and took to their heels, the lion meantime roaring terribly and lashing the ground with his tail: and so he drove the affrighted camels, laden as they were, back to the monastery before him.

So when this surprising sight met the brethren's gaze, the donkey pacing in the van, the lion in like fashion marching in the rear, and the laden beasts in the middle, they slipped quietly away to inform the blessed Jerome. He came out, and benevolently bade them to set open the monastery gate, enjoining them to silence. "Take their loads off these our guests," said he, "the camels, I mean, and the donkey, and bathe their feet and give them fodder, and wait to see what God is minded to show His servants."

Then, when all instructions as to the camels

had been obeyed, began the lion as of old to go here and there in high feather through the cloister, flattening himself at the feet of each several brother and wagging his tail, as though to ask forgiveness for the crime that he had never committed. Whereupon the brethren, full of remorse for the cruel charge they had brought against him, would say to one another, " Behold our trusty shepherd whom so short a while ago we were upbraiding for a greedy ruffian, and God has deigned to send him to us with such a resounding miracle, to clear his character! " Meantime the blessed Jerome, aware of things to come, spoke to the brethren, saying, " Be prepared, my brethren, in all things that are requisite for refreshment: so that those who are about to be our guests may be received, as is fitting, without embarrassment."

His orders duly obeyed, and the brethren chatting with the blessed Jerome, suddenly comes a messenger with the news that there are guests without the gate, desirous to see the Father of the community. At this, the already frequently named Father commanded that the doors of the monastery be opened, and the visitors brought to him. They, however, in spite of this invitation, came in blushing, and prostrated themselves at the feet of the blessed Jerome, entreating forgiveness for their fault. Gently raising them up, he admonished them to enjoy their own with thanksgiving, but not to encroach on others' goods: and in short to live cautiously, as ever in the presence of God. And this marvellous discourse ended, he bade them accept refreshment, and take again their camels and go their way.

Then with one voice they cried out, " We entreat you, Father, that you will accept, for the lamps in the church and the necessity of the brethren, half of the oil that the camels have brought: because we know and are sure that it was rather to be of service to you than for our own profit that we went down into Egypt to bargain there." To which the blessed Jerome replied, " This that you ask is indeed not right, for it would seem a great hardship that we who ought to have compassion on others and relieve their necessities by our own giving, should bear so heavy on you, taking your property away from you when we are not in need of it."

To which they answer: " Neither this food,

nor any of our own property do we touch, unless you first command that what we ask shall be done. And so, as we have said, do you now accept half of the oil that the camels have brought: and we pledge ourselves and our heirs to give to you and those that come after you the measure of oil which is called a hin in each succeeding year."

So therefore, constrained and compelled by the violence of their entreaties, the blessed Jerome commanded that their prayer should be fulfilled. They partook of refreshment, and after receiving both benediction and camels, they returned exultant and jocund to their own people. But that these things were done at Bethlehem, and the fashion of their doing, is confidently related among the inhabitants of that place until this day.

THE SAINTS OF THE WEST

THE DEATH OF KING TEUDIRIC

K ING TEUDIRIC had kept peace and
justice with his people for the years that
he held kingship, till such time as he laid
aside the temporal power for ever, in that
he commended his kingdom to his son Mouric,
and began to live a hermit life in the cliffs of
Tintern. But while he was in that life, the Sax-
ons began to invade his land against Mouric his
son, and beyond himself there was none to help,
that his son might not be driven from his in-
heritance by strangers. Of Teudiric it was said
in the days when he held his kingdom that never
had he been vanquished by the enemy but ever
was the victor, and that once his face was seen
in the battle-line straightway the enemy were
driven to flight. And the night before, the angel
of the Lord said to him : " To-morrow go to the
help of the people of God against the enemies
of the Church of Christ, and the foe shall turn
their face in flight as far as Brockwere, and do
thou stand armed in the battle-line, and when
thy face as in time past is seen and known, they
shall take to flight. And hereafter for XXX
years they shall not dare to come against thy

country in thy son's time, and the men of thy
land and their sons that come after them shall
be in quiet peace: and thou thyself shalt be
wounded with a thrust above Tintern, and after
three days thou shalt die in peace."

So in the morning he rose as the army of
Mouric, his son, came by, and he mounted his
horse and rode with them, joyous of the bidding
of the angel. And he stood in armour in the
battle-line above the bank of the Wye near Tintern ford. And at the sight of his face they
turned their backs and fled, yet one of them
hurled a lance and the lance wounded him even
as he had been told, and he rejoiced over it, as
a man rejoices over the rout of his foe and the
taking of the spoil. Then Mouric, his son, returning victorious with the captured spoil,
would have his father come with him. And he
said, " I will not go from this place until my
Lord Jesus Christ shall bear me hence to the
place of my desire, to the island of Echni, where
I have willed to lie after my death."

And in the morning at dawn there were two
stags yoked and ready with his bier before his
lodging. And the man of God, knowing that
they were sent on God's behalf, ascended the
bier; and wherever they rested, there springs

42

welled up, until they came to a place beside a meadow towards the Severn Sea. And after they had come to that place, a spring of clearest water welled up and swept the bier asunder, and straightway he commended his soul to God and bade the stags depart: and there he remained alone, and after a while gave up the ghost.

ST. COLUMBA AND THE CRANE

AND another time it befell, while the Saint was living on Iona, that he called one of the brethren to him, to speak to him. " Go thou," he said, " three days from now to the west of this island at dawn, and sit above the shore and wait: for when the third hour before sunset is past, there shall come flying from the northern coasts of Ireland a stranger guest, a crane, wind tossed and driven far from her course in the high air: tired out and weary she will fall on the beach at thy feet and lie there, her strength nigh gone: tenderly lift her and carry her to the steading near by: make her welcome there and cherish her with all care for three days and nights; and when the three days are ended, refreshed and loath to tarry longer with us in our exile, she shall take flight again towards that old sweet land of Ireland whence she came, in pride of strength once more: and if I commend her so earnestly to thy charge, it is that in that countryside where thou and I were reared, she too was nested."

The brother obeyed: and on the third day,

when the third hour before sunset was past, stood as he was bidden, in wait for the coming of the promised guest: and when she had come and lay fallen on the beach, he lifted her and carried her ailing to the steading, and fed her, famished as she was. And on his return that evening to the monastery the Saint spoke to him, not as one questioning but as one speaks of a thing past. " May God bless thee, my son," said he, " for thy kind tending of this pilgrim guest: that shall make no long stay in her exile, but when three suns have set shall turn back to her own land."

And the thing fell out even as the Saint had foretold. For when her three days housing was ended, and as her host stood by, she rose in first flight from the earth into high heaven, and after a while at gaze to spy out her aerial way, took her straight flight above the quiet sea, and so to Ireland through the tranquil weather.

45

ST. COLUMBA AND THE WHITE HORSE

ON a day in the month of May, the old man set out to visit the brethren at their work: and weary with the years that were upon him, he made the journey in a cart. He found them busy in the western fields of the island: and that day he spoke to them. "I had a great longing on me," he said, "this April just now past, in the high days of the Easter feast, to go to the Lord Christ:

46

and it was granted me by Him, if I so willed. But I would not have the joy of your feast turned into mourning, and so I willed to put off the day of my going from the world a little longer." But at this heavy saying his monks were sorely downcast, and he began to hearten them as well as he might. And that done, sitting as he was in the cart, and turning his face to the east, he blessed the island and the islanders that dwelt upon it; and from that day, as is written in the book I have already spoken of, the poison in the triple-forked tongue of the viper has done no hurt to man or to beast, until this day. And so he uttered the words of his blessing, and was carried back to his monastery. . . .

At the end of that same week, that is on the Saturday, the venerable old man and his faithful Diarmid who tended him set out to the blessing of a barn near by. And going inside, the Saint blessed it, and two heaps of grain that were stored there: and then with a gesture of thanksgiving, he spoke, " Truly," said he, " I give my brethren at home joy that this year, if so be I might have to go somewhere away from you, you will have what provision will last you the year."

47

But at that, Diarmid his man began to grieve, and said, " You have saddened us too often this year, my father, with this talk of yours about going away." And the Saint made answer, " I have a small secret word to say to you; and if you would give me your promise to reveal it to no one before my death, I could tell you more openly about my going." And when the asked for promise had been given, his man kneeling before him, the saintly old man spoke. " In the Holy Book," he said, " this day is called the Sabbath, which is, being interpreted, rest. And truly is this day my Sabbath, for it is the last day for me of this present toilsome life, when from all weariness of travail I shall take my rest, and at midnight of this Lord's Day that draws on, I shall as the Scripture saith, go the way of my fathers. For now my Lord Jesus Christ hath deigned to invite me; and to Him, I say, at this very midnight and at His own desiring, I shall go. For so it was revealed to me by the Lord himself." At this sad hearing his man began bitterly to weep, and the Saint tried to comfort him as best he might.

And so the Saint left the barn, and took the road back to the monastery: and halfway

48

there sat down to rest. Afterwards on that spot they set a cross, planted upon a millstone, and it is to be seen by the roadside to this day. And as the Saint sat there, a tired old man taking his rest awhile, up runs the white horse, his faithful servitor that used to carry the milk pails, and coming up to the Saint he leaned his head against his breast and began to mourn, knowing as I believe from God Himself—for to God every animal is wise in the instinct his Maker hath given him—that his master was soon to go from him, and that he would see his face no more : and his tears ran down as a man's might into the lap of the Saint, and he foamed as he wept. Seeing it, Diarmid would have driven the sorrowing creature away, but the Saint prevented him saying, " Let be, let be, suffer this lover of mine to shed on my breast the tears of his most bitter weeping. Behold, you that are a man and have a reasonable soul could in no way have known of my departing if I had not but now told you : yet to this dumb and irrational beast, his Creator in such fashion as pleased Him has revealed that his master is to go from him." And so saying, he blessed the sad horse that had served him, and it turned again to its way.

E

ST. COLUMBAN IN THE VOSGES

IT was in these parts it befell that while the saint was walking in the dark woods, a book on his shoulder, and arguing with himself about Holy Writ, the thought came suddenly to his mind whether he would rather choose to suffer the outrage of men, or the savagery of beasts. His thought drove him hard, and he would often cross himself and pray: and finally he said to himself that it was better to suffer the ferocity of wild beasts that was no sin of theirs, than the cruelty of men, to the loss of their own souls. And even as he turned this over in his mind, he saw twelve wolves come towards him, and stand about him on the right hand and on the left, himself in the midst: and he stood motionless, saying, " God, look to my help: Lord, make haste to help me." They came nearer, and their muzzles touched his clothes: and while he stood unshaken, they turned and left him there unterrified, and on to their ranging of the wood.

So, this assay of his endurance past and he secure, he took his road through the forest. He had not gone far when he heard voices, a gang of Swabian robbers who at that time haunted that countryside: and he heard them go by, prowling in the wood. And so, his constancy again assayed, he defied disaster. But whether this had been a diabolic illusion, or whether it had indeed happened, he could not tell.

Another time he left his cell, and penetrating deeper into these vast solitudes, came upon a monstrous rock, its flanks broken into cliffs and its back jagged with points of rock, untrodden by man: and there he spied a secret hollow cave. He came up closer, to examine the hiding place, and found inside the cave a bear's den, and the bear himself within. He bade the wild creature to go gently away, nor hereafter, said he, return to this mountain pass again. And the bear went gently away, nor ever dared return. The place is about seven miles, more or less, from Annegrey. . . .

Yet marvel not that bird and beast should obey the command of the man of God. For Chamnoald, now in the episcopal purple at Lyons, and once his servant and disciple, is evidence for it: he used to tell that he often saw him when he would have gone walking in the woods to fast or to pray, how he would call the creatures of the wild, birds or beasts, to him, and how they would come at once to his call, and he would stroke them with his hand and caress them: and the wild things and the birds would leap and frisk about him for sheer happiness, jumping up on him as young dogs jump on their masters. Even that small wild creature that men call in the vulgar tongue the squirrel, would come at his call from the high tree-tops, and the saint would take it in his hand and set it on his shoulder, and it would be running in and out of the folds of his cowl: and this the aforesaid bishop said he had often seen.

ST. MALO AND THE SOW

At one time when he was going up and down through Brittany to sow the seed of the divine word in the field of the husbandry of God, he came upon a swineherd in a meadow, twisted with bitter grief. He had been herding a drove of pigs, and a greedy unmannerly sow among them was destroying a field of standing corn, and he, trying to save his neighbour's crop, had thrown an ill-directed stone at her and killed her. And now he was in dread of his lord's wrath on his offence, and what he knew would put a keener edge upon it was the seven piglings trotting about, trying to draw milk as of old from their dead mother's dugs, and able to find no stay for their own lives from that lifeless body. St. Malo, whose heart had room only for compassion, could not watch the swineherd's tears without tears himself: and pouring out a prayer to God, he laid his staff on the ear of the dead sow, and raising her up by that sole touch, he brought back joy to the mourner. The swineherd told the story to his master, and had the praises of the

53

servant of God in every man's mouth. And the master, mounting his horse, came to give his thanks to the saint, face to face, and offered one of his farms to the church, for the use, under him, of the servants of God.

ST. MALO AND THE WREN

AND another miracle he wrought like to this, worthy of record for its compassion alone. He was a follower of Paul the Apostle, whose own hands supplied his wants, if aught were lacking: and when he had leisure from his task of preaching the Gospel, he kept himself by the work of his hands. One day he was busy with the brethren in the vineyard, pruning the vines, and for better speed in his work took off his cloak and laid it out of sight. When his work was done and he came to take his cloak, he found that the small bird whom common folk call a wren had laid an egg on it. And knowing that God's care is not far from the birds, since not one of them falls on the ground without the Father, he let his cloak lie there, till the eggs were hatched and the wren brought out her brood. And this was the marvel, that all the time that cloak lay there, there fell no rain upon it. And whoever came to hear of it, they glorified the power of God, and they praised God's own pity in man.

55

ST. CUTHBERT IN THE SHEILING

ONE day as he rode his solitary way about the third hour after sunrise, he came by chance upon a hamlet a spear's cast from the track, and turned off the road to it. The woman of the house that he went into was the pious mother of a family, and he was anxious to rest there a little while, and to ask some provision for the horse that carried him rather than for himself, for it was the oncoming of winter. The woman brought him kindly in, and was earnest with him that he would let her get ready a meal, for his own comfort, but the man of God denied her. "I must not eat yet," said he, "because to-day is a fast." It was indeed Friday when the faithful for the most part prolong their fast until the third hour before sunset, for reverence of the Lord's Passion. The woman, full of hospitable zeal, insisted. "See now," said she, "the road that you are going, you will find never a clachan or a single house upon it, and indeed you have a long way yet before you, and you will not be at the end of it before sundown. So do, I ask you, take some food before you go, or you will have to keep your fast the whole day, and maybe even till the morrow." But though she pressed him hard, devotion to his religion overcame her entreating, and he went through the day fasting, until evening.

But as twilight fell and he began to see that he could not come to the end of the journey he had planned that day, and that there was no human habitation near where he could stay the night, suddenly as he rode he saw close by a huddle of shepherds' huts, built ramshackle for the summer, and now lying open and deserted. Thither he went in search of shelter, tethered his horse to the inside wall, gathered up a bundle of hay that the wind had torn from the thatch, and set it before him for fodder. Himself had begun to say his hours, when suddenly in the midst of his chanting of the Psalms he saw his horse rear up his head and begin cropping the thatch of the hovel and dragging it down, and in the middle of the falling thatch came tumbling a linen cloth lapped up: curious to know what it might be, he finished his prayer, came up and found wrapped in the linen cloth a piece of loaf still hot, and meat, enough for one man's meal.

And chanting his thanks for heaven's grace, " I thank God," said he, " Who has stooped to make a feast for me that was fasting for love of His Passion, and for my comrade." So he divided the piece of loaf that he had found, and gave half to the horse, and the rest he kept for himself to eat, and from that day he was the readier to fasting because he understood that the meal had been prepared for him in the solitude by His gift Who of old fed Elijah the solitary in like fashion by the birds, when there was no man near to minister to him; Whose eyes are on them that fear Him and that hope in His mercy, that He will snatch their souls from death and cherish them in their hunger. And this story I had from a brother of our monastery which is at the mouth of the river Wear, a priest, Ingwald by name, who has the grace of his great age rather to contemplate things eternal with a pure heart than things temporal with the eyes of earth: and he said that he had it from Cuthbert himself, the time that he was Bishop.

ST. CUTHBERT AND THE OTTERS

I T was his way for the most part to wander in those places and to preach in those remote hamlets, perched on steep rugged mountain sides, where other men would have a dread of going, and whose poverty and rude ignorance gave no welcome to any scholar. . . . Often for a whole week, sometimes for two or three, and even for a full month, he would not return home, but would abide in the mountains, and call these simple folk to heavenly things by his word and his ways. . . .

[*He was, moreover, easily entreated, and came to stay at the abbey of Coldingham on a cliff above the sea.*]

As was his habit, at night while other men

took their rest, he would go out to pray: and after long vigils kept far into the night, he would come home when the hour of common prayer drew near. One night, a brother of this same monastery saw him go silently out, and stealthily followed on his track, to see where he was going or what he would do. And so he went out from the monastery and, his spy following him, went down to the sea, above which the monastery was built: and wading into the depths till the waves swelled up to his neck and arms, kept his vigil through the dark with chanting voiced like the sea. As the twilight of dawn drew near, he waded back up the beach, and kneeling there, again began to pray: and as he prayed, straight from the depths of the sea came two four-footed beasts which are called by the common people otters. These, prostrate before him on the sand, began to busy themselves warming his feet with pantings, and trying to dry them with their fur: and when this good office was rendered, and they had his benediction, they slipped back again beneath their native waters. He himself returned home, and sang the hymns of the office with the brethren at the appointed hour. But the brother who had stood watching him from the cliffs was seized with such panic that he could hardly make his way home, tottering on his feet: and early in the morning came to him and fell at his feet, begging forgiveness with his tears for his foolish attempt, never doubting but that his behaviour of the night was known and discovered.

To whom Cuthbert: "What ails you, my brother? What have you done? Have you been out and about to try to come at the truth of this night wandering of mine ? I forgive you, on this one condition: that you promise to tell no man what you saw, until my death." . . . And the promise given, he blessed the brother and absolved him alike of the fault and the annoyance his foolish boldness had given: and the brother kept silence on the piece of valour that he had seen, until after the saint's death, when he took pains to tell it to many.

ST. CUTHBERT AND THE RAVENS ON THE FARNES

S O, in that same monastery [of Lindisfarne] he fulfilled many years: and at last, with the good will of his abbot and his brethren to company him, he set out in deep delight towards that secret solitude for which he had so long desired and sought and striven. The coming and going of the active life had done its long work upon him, and he rejoiced that now he had earned his right to climb to the quiet of meditation upon God: happy that he had at last come in sight of their lot, of whom it is sung in the Psalms: " *They go from strength to strength: every one of them in Zion appeareth before God. . . .*"

There is an island called Farne, set in the sea—not like that part of the coast where live the men of Lindisfarne, which twice a day by the upswelling of the ocean tide (which in Greek is called *rheuma*) becomes an island, and twice a day, its shores again bared by the tide outgoing, is restored to its neighbour the land—but hidden several miles to the east of this half-island, and sieged on this side and on that by the deep and infinite sea. No man, before God's servant Cuthbert, had been able to make his dwelling here alone, for the phantoms of demons that haunted it: but at the coming of Christ's soldier, armed with the helmet of salvation, the shield of faith and the sword of the Spirit which is the word of God, the fiery darts of the wicked fell quenched, and the foul Enemy himself, with all his satellite mob, was put to flight.

And so Christ's soldier, made by the rout of the tyrannous host king of this land he had set foot on, founded a city to match his kingship, and built houses to match his city. The building was all but round, measuring from wall to wall about four or five perches: outside, the wall rose higher than a standing man: but inside, by cutting away the living rock, he made it much higher, to the end that all wantonness of eye and thought constrained and the whole intent of the mind upreared to high desire, the holy inhabitant could see nothing from his dwelling but the sky. This wall he built, not of hewn stone nor of mortar and brick, but of rough boulders and turf which he had digged within, and carried: some of these indeed so huge that one would hardly think four men could lift them, and yet he is known to have carried them hither with angelic help and set them into the wall. He had two houses in his enclosure, one an oratory, the other a dwelling place for the common uses of living. The partition walls he made mostly of plain earth by digging and hewing within and without; and on them he set a roof of rough beams and thatch. At the harbour of the island was a larger house in which the brethren when they came to visit him could be received and take their rest, and not far off was a well handy for their occasions. . . .

At first indeed he would accept a scant portion of bread from them, and would drink from his well: but after a while he felt it was more fit that he should live by the work of his own hand, after the example of the Fathers. So he asked them to bring him tools to dig the ground with, and wheat to sow: but the grain that he had sown in spring showed no sign of a crop even by the middle of the summer. So when the brethren as usual were visiting him the man of God said, " It may be the nature of the soil, or it may be it is not the will of God that any wheat should grow for me in

64

this place: so bring me, I pray you, barley, and perhaps I may raise some harvest from it. But if God will give it no increase, it would be better for me to go back to the community than be supported here on other men's labours." They brought him the barley, and he committed it to the ground, far past the time of sowing, and past all hope of springing: and soon there appeared an abundant crop. When it began to ripen, then came the birds, and it was who among them should devour the most. So up comes God's good servant, as he would afterwards tell—for many a time, with his benign and joyous regard, he would tell in company some of the things that he himself had won by faith, and so strengthen the faith of his hearers— "And why," says he, "are you touching a crop you did not sow? Or is it, maybe, that you have more need of it than I? If you have God's leave, do what He allows you: but if not, be off, and do no more damage to what is not your own." He spoke, and at the first word of command, the birds were off in a body and come what might for ever after they contained themselves from any trespass on his harvests. . . .

F

And here might be told a miracle done by the blessed Cuthbert in the fashion of the aforesaid Father, Benedict, wherein the obedience and humility of birds puts to shame the obstinacy and arrogance of men. Upon that island for a great while back a pair of ravens had had their dwelling: and one day at their nesting time the man of God spied them tearing with their beaks at the thatch on the brethren's hospice of which I have spoken, and carrying off pieces of it in their bill to build their nest. He thrust at them gently with his hand, and bade them give over this damage to the brethren. And when they scoffed at his command, " In the name of Jesus Christ," said he, " be off with you as quick as ye may, and never more presume to abide in the place which ye have spoiled." And scarcely had he spoken, when they flew dismally away.

But toward the end of the third day, one of the two came back, and finding Christ's servant busy digging, comes with his wings lamentably trailing and his head bowed to his feet, and his voice low and humble, and begs pardon with such signs as he might: which the good father well understanding, gives him permission to return.

66

As for the other, leave once obtained, he straight goes off to fetch his mate, and with no tarrying, back they both come, and carrying along with them a suitable present, no less than a good sized hunk of hog's lard such as one greases axles with: many a time thereafter the man of God would show it the brethren who came to see him, and would offer it to grease their shoes, and he would urge on them how obedient and humble men should be, when the proudest of birds made haste with prayers and lamentation and presents to atone for the insult he had given to man. And so, for an example of reformed life to men, these did abide for many years thereafter on that same island, and built their nest, nor ever wrought annoyance upon any.

67

ST. WERBURGA OF CHESTER AND THE WILD GEESE

IT was in the city of Chester that the girl Werburga, daughter of Wulfhere, King of Mercia, and Ermenhild . . . took her vows, and her goodness shone for many years. The story of one miracle done by her I now shall tell, which made a great stir and was long told about the countryside. She had a farm outside the walls, where the wild geese would come and destroy the standing corn in the fields. The steward in charge of the farm took all shifts to drive them off, but with small success. And so, when he came to wait upon his lady, he added his complaint of them to the other tales he would tell her of the day. "Go," said she, "and shut them all into a house." The countryman, dumbfounded at the oddness of the command, thought that his lady was jesting: but finding her serious and insistent, went back to the field where he had first spied the miscreants, and bade them, speaking loud and clear, to do their lady's bidding and come after him. Whereupon with one accord they gathered themselves into a flock, and walking with down bent necks after their enemy, were shut up under a roof. On one of them, however, the rustic, with no thought of any to accuse him, made bold to dine.

At dawn came the maid, and after scolding the birds for pillaging other people's property, bade them take their flight. But the winged creatures knew that one of their company was missing: nor did they lack wit to go circling round their lady's feet, refusing to budge further, and complaining as best they could, to excite her compassion. She, through God's revealing, and convinced that all this clamour was not without cause, turned her gaze upon the steward, and divined the theft. She bade him gather up the bones and bring them to her. And straightway, at a healing sign from the girl's hand, skin and flesh began to come upon the bones, and feathers to fledge upon the skin, till the living bird, at first with eager hop and soon upon the wing, launched itself into the air. Nor were the others slow to follow it, their numbers now complete, though first they made obeisance to their lady and deliverer. And so the merits of this maid are told at Chester, and her miracles extolled.

Yet though she be generous and swift to answer all men's prayers, yet most gracious is her footfall among the women and boys, who pray as it might be to a neighbour and a woman of their own countryside.

ST. BENNO AND THE FROG

IT was often the habit of the man of God to
go about the fields in meditation and prayer:
and once as he passed by a certain marsh,
a talkative frog was croaking in its slimy
waters: and lest it should disturb his contemplation, he bade it to be a Seraphian, inasmuch as all the frogs in Seraphus are mute. But
when he had gone on a little way, he called to
mind the saying in Daniel: "*O ye whales and*

71

all that move in the waters, bless ye the Lord. O all ye beasts and cattle, bless ye the Lord." And fearing lest the singing of the frogs might perchance be more agreeable to God than his own praying, he again issued his command to them, that they should praise God in their accustomed fashion: and soon the air and the fields were vehement with their conversation.

ST. GODRIC AT FINCHALE

I MYSELF as a small boy saw the great
Godric, I a youngster and he an old man,
and the high memory of it is sweet in my
mind. He was small enough in body, but
his spirit had the height of heaven. In
youth indeed his hair was black, but in his
old age, of an angelic whiteness : a broad
forehead, sparkling eyes, heavy eyebrows
that almost met, broad shoulders, a lean
body, thin with fasting. . . . He was a
monk of Durham, and for sixty years lived
a hermit : he died an old man and full of
days in his chosen dwelling place in Finchale :
and being dead, his virtue speaketh. . . .

Finchale, the place where the man of God
accomplished his warfare, was thought to
have its name in ancient days from a King
called Finc. The sound of this name seems
to speak a certain harshness in the British
tongue which is unknown in our own. The
ancients say that here of old time lived
Finc, King of Britain, and that he built
greatly here. Indeed, hidden under the
green grass are the traces of ruined

foundations, and where the ground is digged deeper, the questing spade many a time uncovers the crowding bones of the dead, in the womb of the earth itself. Whence is it plain that here were once the thronging habitations of men, to which this vision of burial places and of foundations is testimony beyond our doubting.

The Wear, a river that is rich and teeming with many kinds of fish, flows round this spot, circling it round on east and north and west : and no part of it is free from the river save the south only. Access to this lap of earth is indeed possible, but it easily escapes the knowledge and the inroads of the chance wayfarer : for on the southern side, by which it is approached, it is hemmed in by the dense shadow of a wood of tall trees, through which at this time there was no track, save only such devious and circuitous ways as the wild creatures use, wandering and cropping here and there through the wood. The place is sunk in a deep valley, and on the further bank, across the river which washes these three sides, great cliffs and mountains hem it in and circle it around : while from these peaks and chasms a shadow falls that grows and lengthens as though itself were a vast mountain. To one who stands below and gazes up, the mountains seem to rise and overhang like giant towers, a beetling height that casts a strange dread upon the heart. Yet below the sweep of their encircling, there lies in the depth of the valley a stretch of level land, shut in by woods of no great height, but very fair, and in this place, beside the flowing of the teeming river, the man of God began to build the tiny habitations of his going out and coming in. . . .

[*At his first coming he had built an oratory, and one day saw above the altar two young and very lovely maids : the one of them, Mary Magdalene, the other the Mother of God : and the Mother of God put her hand upon his head and taught him to sing after her this prayer :*

Mary Holy Virgin, mother of Jesus Christ
   of Nazareth,
Hold, shield and help thy Godric,
Take him, bring him soon to the Kingdom
   of God with thee.]

75

Thereafter with more devotion than ever he served the Lord : and called upon the most blessed Mother of God, even as he had promised her, in all distress that came about him, and found her most swift to aid. A long time thus spent in solitude, his friends compelled him to take some one to wait on him, and have a better care of his outward affairs. For so intent was he upon prayer, meditation and contemplation that he would spend no labour on things out of doors. At first therefore, a little boy, his brother's son, came to wait upon him, and was with him for eleven years. At that time the only living thing he had about him was a single cow : and because the boy was yet but small and of very tender years, he would often be so drowsy with sleep in the mornings that he would forget to take the beast to pasture, or fetch her again in the evenings : or indeed perhaps the familiar task became a weariness to him.

So one day the man of God went up to the creature, and putting his girdle about her neck, spoke to her as if to one that had reason and intelligence. " Come," said he, " follow me, and go on with me to thy pasture." She went on, and the youngster, looking and listening, followed after them. And again the saint spoke. " I command thee, in the Lord's name," said he, " that every day at sunrise thou shalt go forth alone, with no guide, to thy pasture ; and every noon and evening at the fitting time, come home, with no servant to lead thee : and when thine udder with fulness of milk needs easing come to me, wherever I shall be, and when thou art milked, go lightened back to thy pasture, if yet there is time." And, marvel as it is, from that day and thenceforward, the cow went and came at the proper hour, and whenever through the day she was heavy with milk she would come to him : and if by chance he were in church she would stand outside, by the door, lowing and complaining, calling him. And he, his hour of prayer ended, would come out and milk her, and she then go away, wherever he bade her. The boy who saw this, told it : for he grew up, and is now a very old man.

In after days, a little lad came to serve in the house of the man of God, and was set to these outside tasks. And not knowing that the cow was accustomed to obey the saint's command, and finding her one day grazing in the meadow, he began to harry her and prod her with a goad. And she, incensed, turned on the youngster and catching him between her horns, charged off with him in a great heat of indignation, to the door of the house where the man of God was busy within. He came out, took the boy in his arms and lifted him from between her horns, rescuing him unhurt from the wrath of the irate beast.

In this are three works of God which we find singularly admirable: first, that the animal feared to injure or inflict any wound on the servant of her master, but, none the less, by terrifying his boldness and presumption, administered well - deserved punishment: second, that Christ Himself would not have the guileless and ignorant youngster killed, but preserved him by the help of His servant: third, that He made manifest to us the merits of the man of God, in that by his intervention he saved one set amid death from death's very jaws.

This same youngster, now indeed an old man, would often tell the story with thankfulness, praising God who so marvellously deigned to snatch him by the merits of his master from sudden destruction.

ST. GODRIC'S GARDEN AND THE WILD DEER

NOW if one is intent too long upon one task, the mind in tedium very soon revolts against its undertaking : and so the man of God would turn the energy of his mind to various activities, yet seldom did he suspend his soul from prayer. He had rooted up from the ground near by the unprofitable undergrowth of the wood, and now began upon the tree trunks that were left to graft in cuttings of fruit trees which he had obtained from his visitors, and very skilful he was, and had made for himself a kind of enclosed orchard. In summer, when the tender shoots come to life again with green leaves, the branches he had grafted in began to swell and gradually here and there fragile sprays of green and young leaves appeared. But the unaccustomed sweetness of them was very tempting to the wild things of the wood, and they began very greedily to crop this strange new greenness, and most assiduous they were in visiting this agreeable pasture. They would nip off

the sprays of the apple boughs, and gnaw
the tender juicy bark and scatter with their
hooves the young saplings : and not a single
kind of tree, of those he had grafted with so
much pains, did these wild creatures of the
wood suffer to come to maturity, in their
unbridled greed.

So one day coming out of his oratory he
saw a wild stag from the wood cropping the
tender leafage of his trees, scattering and
spoiling with all its heart : and making his
way towards the creature, he bade it with
a crook of his finger not to run away from
the spot, but to wait till he came, without
stirring. Oh strange and stupendous mystery!
The stag, this wild thing of the woods, that
knew no discretion, understood the will of
the man of God from his gesture alone, and
standing still it began trembling all over, as
if it knew that it had offended the soul of
the man of God. Its extreme tremor and
fear went to his heart, and he checked the
wrath in his mind and the blows he had
meant to inflict : and the creature dropped
on its knees as he came, and bowed its head,
to ask pardon as best it could for its bold
trespass. He ungirt his belt, and put it

round the neck of the kneeling animal, and
so led him beyond the bounds of his orchard,
and there releasing him bade him go free
wherever he willed. . . .

It was not long after when lo! a herd of the
woodland creatures came crowding again:
they leapt across the fence, they tore off the
tender flowers and delicate leaves, and every
one of the slips of apple trees that he
had watched over from the beginning and
planted or grafted in his garden, they set
themselves to root up and break off and
trample underfoot. He came out of the
house, and ordered the whole mob to leave
the place : and seizing a rod, he struck one
of them thrice on the flank and leading her
to the trees that lay along the ground, he
showed her rather by signs than by any
spoken word what damage her herd had
done to his planting. Then, raising both
hand and voice, " In the name of Jesus of
Nazareth," said he, " be off and away as
quickly as ye may, nor be so bold as to
come near this garden of mine to its hurt,
until these trees are full-grown : for the
slips of fruit trees that I have grafted on
these trunks I meant for the food of men and

not of beasts." And so saying, he threatened the rest of the dumb creatures with the rod that he held in his hand. And thereupon the whole herd, with heads down bent and stepping delicately, went out : and where they had rioted prancing here and there and leapt in great bounds, they now went forth stepping as it were on tiptoe, with swift-hurrying hoofs. He drove the whole herd to the depth of the forest : and such as lagged behind in weariness, he set his arms about and gently brought them out, making a way for them by lifting a hurdle from his fence. From that time forth never any forest creature dared to trespass the bounds which he had fixed. . . .

Bears, too, would come from the depth of the forest to eat the honey of his bees, and he would find them out and chastise them with the stick that he always carried in his hand. And at a word from him the unwieldy creatures would roar and run, and creatures that no steel blade could daunt would go in terror of a blow from his light rod.

ST. GODRIC AND ST. JOHN THE BAPTIST'S SALMON

I T was the serene and joyous weather of high summer, and the turning of the year brought nigh the solemn feast of St. John the Baptist. And because the man of God had begged it, and it was the familiar custom, two brothers from the monastery at Durham were sent out to him to celebrate the divine office with all due honour. The office reverently said, and this most solemn Mass ended, the folk who had come for the Feast made their way home ; and the brethren came to him to ask his blessing, and leave to return to their monastery.

" Ye may have God's blessing," said he, " but when St. Cuthbert's sons have come to visit me, they must not go home without their dinner " : and, calling his serving-man, " Quick, beloved," said he, " and set up the table, for these brethren are to eat with us this day."

The table was set up, and oat cake laid upon it, such as he had, and bowls of good milk. Yet when he looked at the feast, it

84

seemed to him but poor, and he bade the serving-man bring fish as well.

"Master," said he in amaze, "where should we get fish at a time like this, in all this heat and drought, when we can see the very bottom of the river? We can cross dry shod where we used to spread the seine and the nets." But he answered, "Go quickly and spread my seine in that same dry pool." The man went out and did as he was told: but with no hope of any sort of catch.

He came back, declaring that the pool had dried up till the very sands of it were parched; and his master bade him make haste to fill the cauldron with water, and set it on the hearth to heat, and this was done. After a little while he bade his man go to the bank and bring back his catch: the man went and looked, and came back empty-handed: he did it again a second time: and then in disgust, refused to go any more. For a little while the man of God held his peace, and then spoke. "Now go this time," said he, "for this very hour the fish has come into the net, that St. John the Baptist promised me; for never could he break a promise by not doing what he said, although

85

our sluggish faith deserved it little. And look you," said he, " but that salmon that is now caught in the seine is a marvellous fine one." So in the end his man went off, and found even as he had been told : and drawing it out of the net, he brought the fish alive to where his master sat in the oratory, and laid it at his feet. Then, as he was bidden, he cut it into pieces and put it into the pot now boiling on the hearth, and cooked it well, and brought it and set it before the brethren at table, and well were they fed and mightily amazed. For they marvelled how a fish could come swimming up a river of which the very sands were dry: and, above all, how the man of God, talking with them and sitting in the oratory could have seen, by the revelation of the spirit, the very hour when the fish entered the meshes of the net. To which he made reply, " St. John the Baptist never deserts his own, but sheds the blessing of his great kindness on those that trust in him." And so he sent them home, well fed and uplifted at so amazing a miracle : praising and glorifying God, who alone doeth marvels, for all that they had seen and heard.

86

ST. GODRIC AND THE HARE

HE had planted vegetables to feed poor men, and these a little hare used stealthily to devour. He put up with the damage for a long time : but at last the track of its paws betrayed the person of the delinquent : and he came on the thief in his garden, and as it turned in headlong flight he bade it halt. The poor little creature stopped, and waited in trembling and alarm the arrival of its pursuer. The Saint caught it, struck it with his rod, and binding a bundle of vegetables on its shoulders sent it off, with these words : "See to it that neither thyself not any of thy acquaintance come to this place again : nor dare to encroach on what was meant for the need of the poor." And so it befel. . . .

The gentleness of his heart did not betray itself only in kindness to men, but his wise solicitude watched over the very reptiles and the creatures of the earth. For in winter when all about was frozen stiff in the cold, he would go out barefoot, and if he lighted on any animal helpless with misery of the

cold, he would set it under his armpit or
in his bosom to warm it. Many a time
would the kind soul go spying under the
thick hedges or tangled patches of briars,
and if haply he found a creature that had
lost its way, or cowed with the harshness of
the weather, or tired, or half dead, he would
recover it with all the healing art he had. . . .

And if anyone in his service had caught a
bird or little beast in a snare or a trap or a
noose, as soon as he found it he would snatch
it from their hands and let it go free in the
fields or the glades of the wood. So that many
a time they would hide their captive spoils
under a corn measure or a basket or some more
secret hiding-place still : but even so they
could never deceive him or keep it hidden.
For often without any telling, and indeed
with his serving-man disavowing and pro-
testing, he would go straight to the place
where the creatures had been hidden : and
while the man would stand by crimson with
fear and confusion, he would lift them out
and set them free. So, too, hares and other
beasts fleeing from the huntsmen he would
take in, and house them in his hut : and
when the ravagers, their hope frustrated,

would be gone, he would send them away to
their familiar haunts. Many a time the
dumb creatures of the wood would swerve
aside from where the huntsmen lay in wait,
and take shelter in the safety of his hut : for
it may be that by some divine instinct they
knew that a sure refuge abided their coming.

ST. GODRIC AND THE HUNTED STAG

IN the time of Rainulf, Bishop of Durham,
certain of his household had come out for
a day's hunting, with their hounds, and
were following a stag which they had singled
out for its beauty. The creature, hard
pressed by the clamour and the baying,
made for Godric's hermitage, and seemed
by its plaintive cries to beseech his help.
The old man came out, saw the stag shiver-
ing and exhausted at his gate, and moved
with pity bade it hush its moans, and
opening the door of his hut, let it go in. The
creature dropped at the good father's feet,
but he, feeling that the hunt was coming
near, came out, shut the door behind him
and sat down in the open : while the dogs,
vexed at the loss of their quarry, turned
back with a mighty baying upon their
masters. They, none the less, following on
the track of the stag, circled round about
the place, plunging through the well-nigh
impenetrable brushwood of thorns and
briars ; and hacking a path with their
blades, came upon the man of God in his

poor rags. They questioned him about the stag : but he would not be the betrayer of his guest, and he made prudent answer, " God knows where he may be." They looked at the angelic beauty of his countenance, and in reverence for his holiness, they fell before him and asked his pardon for their bold intrusion. Many a time afterwards they would tell what had befallen them there, and marvel at it, and by their oft telling of it, the thing was kept in memory by those that came after. But the stag kept house with Godric until the evening : and then he let it go free. But for years thereafter it would turn from its way to visit him, and lie at his feet, to show what gratitude it could for its deliverance.

ST. CUTHBERT'S BIRDS AND BAR-
THOLOMEW, THE HERMIT OF FARNE

FROM ancient time long past, this island has been inhabited by certain birds whose name and race miraculously persists. At the time of year for building nests, they gather here. And such gracious gentleness have they learned from the holiness of the place, or rather from those who made the place holy by their way of living there, that they have no shrinking from the handling or the gaze of men. They love quiet, and yet no clamour disturbs them. Their nests are built everywhere. Some brood above their eggs beside the altar. No man presumes to molest them or touch the eggs without leave. . . . And they in turn do harm to no man's store for food. They seek it with their mates upon the waves of the sea. The ducklings, once they are reared, follow behind their mothers who lead the way, and once they have entered their native waters, come no more back to the nest. The mothers too, their mild and gentle way of life forgotten, receive their ancient state and instinct with the sea. This is the high prerogative of the island, which, had it come to the knowledge of the scholars of old time, would have had its fair fame blazoned through the earth.

But at one time it befel, whilst a mother was leading her brood, herself going on before, that one of the youngsters fell down a cleft of a creviced rock. The mother stood by in distress, and let no one doubt but that she was then endowed with human reason. For she forthwith turned about, left her youngsters behind, came to Bartholomew, and began tugging at the hem of his cloak with her beak, as if to say plainly: " Get up and follow me and give me back my son." He rose at once for her, thinking that he must be sitting on her nest. But as she kept on tugging more and more, he perceived at last that she was asking something from him that she could not come at by voice. And indeed her action was eloquent, if not her discourse. On she went, she first and he after, till coming to the cliff she pointed to the place with her bill, and gazing at Bartholomew, intimated with what signs she could that he was to peer inside. Coming closer, he saw the duckling with its small wings clinging to the rock, and climbing down he brought it back to its mother, who in high delight seemed by her joyous look to give him

94

thanks. Whereupon she took to the water with her sons, and Bartholomew, dumb with astonishment, went back to his oratory.

THE SAINTS OF IRELAND

H

ST. CIARAN AND THE NESTING BIRD

THE most blessed Ciaran, bishop, and first begotten of the Saints of Ireland, belonged to the west border of Leinster, which is called Ossory. At the time that he was born, all the folk of Ireland were heathen. His father was called Luaigne, of the nobler of the Ossory clan : his mother Liadain, born in the south of Munster.... And Ciaran was born and brought up in Corca Laighde, on Cape Clear Island. And verily God chose him from his mother's womb : for when the name of Christ was not yet heard in Ireland, the austerity of the Christian faith began to spring in him. For his parents wondered, and all who saw him, at the soberness of his mind, the gentleness of his nature, the sweetness of his words, his timely fasting, his wise counsels, and the other qualities that belonged to holy men.

One day on this same Cape Clear Island this first of St. Ciaran's miracles came by God's will to pass. For when he was still a lad, a hawk swept down from the sky upon a small bird brooding on its nest and caught it, before St. Ciaran's eyes, and carried it off in its talons into the air. The lad saw it, and was in sore grief over it, and prayed for the poor captive : and straightway the ravisher came down with his prey, and laid the small bird, mangled and halfdead, before him. But under the pitying gaze of the lad, the hapless creature by God's grace was made whole, to his heart's desire : and before his eyes sat brooding on her nest, happy and unhurt.

ST. CIARAN AND BROTHER FOX
AND BROTHER BADGER

FOR thirty years St. Ciaran lived in Ireland, in holiness and integrity of body and soul, without baptism, for the Irish were yet heathen, as we have already said. Nevertheless, by the inspiration of the Holy Ghost in His holy servant Ciaran, he lived devout and perfect in his ways. And hearing a report of the Christian faith in the city of Rome, he left Ireland, and set out to Rome. And on reaching it, he was baptised, and taught in the Catholic faith : and there he remained for twenty years, reading the Holy Scriptures, and collecting books of them, and earnestly studying ecclesiastical discipline. And the Roman people seeing the wisdom and the prudence, the devotion and the faith of Ciaran, the man of God, ordained him bishop there : and then he was sent to Ireland, his own land. And on the road through Italy there met him St. Patrick, archbishop of all Ireland, and the saints of God met face to face and were glad. St. Patrick was not at this time bishop, but was afterwards ordained by Pope Celestine, and sent to Ireland to preach. For him, although there were saints before him in Ireland, God kept the mastery and all the primacy of Ireland : since for no man before Patrick did the Kings and chiefs of Ireland believe in God.

And Patrick said to Ciaran, "Go thou to Ireland before me : and make thy way to a well in the heart of Ireland, on the border between the men of the North and the men of the South : it is called Fuaran, the little cold well : and there found thy monastery : for in that place shall thy glory and thy resurrection be." Then said St. Ciaran, "The place where that well is, is unknown to me." And St. Patrick answered him : "Dear brother, go thy way secure, and God shall be with thee : and take this bell to be thy fellow-traveller on thy journey. It shall be dumb until thou hast come to the well I have told thee of. And when thou hast come to it, thy bell shall sound a clear note, and ring sweetly. And after thirty years I shall come to thee in that place." And the two servants of God kissed and blessed one another, and

102

St. Ciaran went on his way towards Ireland, but the blessed Patrick stayed behind in Italy. And from that day St. Ciaran's bell was silent and voiceless until he came to the well of Fuaran, as St. Patrick had foretold.

Now when St. Ciaran was come to Ireland, God guided him to the well of Fuaran, and there the bell of the man of God rang plain and clear, which bell is called Ciaran's *bardan*, and is held in great honour in the town and the whole parish of St. Ciaran. For it is carried through the country to the oath-taking of chieftains, to the defence of the poor, and to the levying of the dues of the monastery of St. Ciaran. The bell was indeed cast for the bishop Germanus, master to St. Patrick. And the well is, as has been said, on the border between the two parts of Ireland, but on the southern side, in Munster, among the clan Hele. And the blessed Ciaran began to live as a hermit there : for the place was a vast solitude and thick with forest. And he built himself a poor cell, that was the beginning of a monastery. And thereafter by God's gift a city grew up, through the grace of St. Ciaran. And all these are called by one name, Sierkieran.

Now at St. Ciaran's first coming to that place, he sat himself down under a tree : and under the shadow of it was a fierce boar. The boar, seeing for the first time the countenance of man, fled in sore terror ; and then, made tame by God, he came back to St. Ciaran as though to be his serving-man : and that boar was St. Ciaran's first disciple or monk, as one might say, in that place. For straightway that boar, as the man of God watched, began with great vigour tearing down twigs and grass with his teeth to build him a little cell. At that time there was no one with the saint : he had left his disciples behind him and escaped alone to that solitude. Later on other animals came from their dens in the wilds to St. Ciaran, a fox, and a badger, and a wolf and a deer: and they stayed with him, tame and gentle. And they obeyed the saint's word in all things, as if they had been his monks.

But one day the Fox who was shrewder and wilier than the other animals, stole his abbot's shoes and abandoning his vow, carried them off to his ancient dwelling in the forest : intending to chew them there. Knowing this, the good Father sent another monk or disciple, namely the Badger, into the forest after the Fox, to bring back his brother to his post. So the Badger, being well learned in the woods, at once set out in obedience to his abbot's bidding, and took his way straight to the den of Brother Fox. There finding him about to gnaw his master's slippers, he bit his ears and his tail, and cropped his fur, and forced him to come back with him to his monastery, there to do penance for his theft. And the Fox, necessity driving him, and the Badger with him carrying the shoes none the worse, came about Nones to St. Ciaran in his cell. And the saint said to the Fox, " Wherefore, brother, didst thou do this ill deed, which it becomes not monks to do? Behold, our water is sweet and free to us, and food is here for us all alike to share. And if thou hadst a longing, as is thy nature, to eat flesh, Almighty God would have made it for thee from the roots of these trees, if we had asked Him." Then the Fox entreated his forgiveness, and did penance fasting, and would not eat until he was bidden by the saint. And thereafter he lived sociably with the others.

In the end, St. Ciaran's disciples and many others sought him out from all parts in that place: and it was the beginning of a famous monastery. But the aforesaid animals abode there, for the rest of their lives, tame and familiar, for the saint was fain to see them.

ST. MOLING AND THE FOX

THE blessed bishop Moling used to keep animals both wild and tame about him, in honour of their Maker, and they would eat out of his hand. And among these was a fox. Now one day the fox stole a hen that belonged to the brethren and ate it. The brethren brought their complaint, and the man of God scolded the fox and accused him of being perfidious above other animals. The fox, however, seeing his master wroth with him, gazed upon him with solicitude, and made off to a convent of nuns that were under St. Moling's care, captured a hen by guile, and bringing her to his lord, presented her safe and sound. And the saint, smiling, said to him: "Thou hast offered rapine to atone for theft. Take back this hen to her ladies, and deliver her to them unharmed: and hereafter do thou live without stealing, like the rest of the animals." Hearing this, the fox took the hen between his teeth and deposited her unharmed in her ladies' cloister. And those who saw so great a marvel wrought in either place, made merry over it and blessed God.

Another time another fox stole a book from the brethren, and carried it off to hide it in one of his earths, intending to come back shortly and gnaw it there. But on his return to the monastery, he was found stealing and eating a honeycomb. Whereupon the brethren laid hold on him and brought him to St. Moling, and accused him of stealing the book. And the holy old man bade the brethren to let him go free. And when he was released, the Saint said to him, " O wise and crafty one, be off, and bring me back that book unharmed, and quickly." At that, off went the fox, and hasted to bring the book from his cave, and set it down dry and unharmed before the holy bishop. And then he lay upon the ground before the man of God, as if seeking forgiveness. And the Saint said, " Get up, you wretch, and fear nought: but never touch a book again." And the fox got up rejoicing, and fulfilled in marvellous wise the Saint's behest: for not only did he never touch books again, but if any one would show him a book in jest, he took to flight.

ST. BRENDAN AND THE SEA MONSTERS

AND when the Feast of the blessed Paul the Apostle, who was slain under Nero, was come, they were eager to celebrate his high day with devotion and glory. But while the Abbot was chanting the office, his voice sweet and ringing, the brethren said, " Sing lower, Master ; or we shall be shipwrecked. For the water is so clear that we can see to the bottom, and we see innumerable fishes great and fierce, such as never were discovered to human eye before, and if thou dost anger them with thy chanting, we shall perish."

Then the Abbot upbraided them for fools and laughed a great laugh. " What," said he, " has driven out your faith? Fear naught but the Lord our God, and love Him in fear. Many perils have tried you, but the Lord brought you safely out of them all. There is no danger here. What are ye afraid of? " And turning again, Brendan celebrated Mass more solemnly than before. And thereupon the monsters of the deep began to rise on all sides, and making merry for joy of the Feast, followed after the ship. Yet when the office of the day was ended, they straightway turned back and went their way.

ST. BRENDAN AND THE SEA-CAT

THENCE they sailed to another island, lovely indeed but small, in which there was from old time a whirlpool in which fish might be caught. For the sea withdrawing from it, the creatures of the sea were left behind in it. They went across the island, and found a church built of stone, and in it a venerable old man at his prayers. But wherefore say I an old man ? For he seemed rather to be animated bones. And the old man said to them, " O holy men of God, make haste to flee from this island. For there is a sea-cat here, of old time, inveterate in wiles, that hath grown huge through eating excessively of fish." Thereupon they turned back in haste to their ship, and abandoned the island.

But lo, behind them they saw that beast swimming through the sea, and it had great eyes like vessels of glass. Thereupon they all fell to prayer, and Brendan said, "Lord Jesus Christ, hinder thy beast." And straightway arose another beast from the depths of the sea, and approaching fell to battle with the first : and both went down to the depth of the sea, nor were they further seen. Then they gave thanks to God, and turned back to the old man, to question him as to his way of living and whence he had come. And he said to them, " We were twelve men from the island of Ireland that came to this place, seeking the place of our resurrection. Eleven be dead : and I alone remain, awaiting, O saint of God, the Host from thy hands. We brought with us in the ship a cat, a most amiable cat and greatly loved by us : but he grew to great bulk through the eating of fish, as I said: yet our Lord Jesus Christ did not suffer him to harm us." And then he showed them the way to the land which they sought : and receiving the Host at the hands of Brendan, he fell joyfully asleep in the Lord : and he was buried beside his companions.

ST. BRENDAN AND THE WHITE
BIRDS

AFTER these things they came to an island that was very fair and filled with flowers in bloom and trees in fruit. And when they sought a harbour where they might enter in, they found on the southern coast of the island a little river of sweet water running into the sea, and there they brought their ship to land. . . . Then Brendan said to his brethren, " Behold, our Lord Jesus Christ, the good, the merciful, hath given us this place wherein to abide His holy resurrection. My brothers, if we had naught else to restore our bodies, this spring alone would suffice us for meat and drink."

Now there was above the spring a tree of strange height, covered with birds of dazzling white, so crowded on the tree that scarcely could it be seen by human eyes. And looking upon it the man of God began to ponder within himself what cause had brought so great a multitude of birds together on one tree. And so great was the bewilderment of his thoughts that he prayed

with tears for the revealing of the mystery.
. . . And even as the man of heavenly
desires spoke within himself, behold one of
the birds flew from the tree, and its wings
rang against the ship, like the chiming of a
bell : and perching on the highest part of
the prow of the ship, it began to spread out
its wings in token of inward joy, and to gaze
with a placid regard upon the man of God.
And straightway the man of God knew that
the Lord had given heed to his prayer, and
he spoke to the bird. " Inasmuch," said he,
" as thou art God's servant and His messenger, then tell us whence came ye hither,
and by whom was so mighty a multitude of
birds gathered in one place."

And the bird spoke to him. " We are," it
said, " of that great ruin of the ancient foe,
who did not consent to him wholly. Yet
because we consented in part to his sin, our
ruin also befell. For God is just, and keepeth
truth and mercy. And so by His judgment
He sent us to this place, where we know no
other pain than that we cannot see the presence of God. And so hath He estranged us
from the fellowship of those who stood firm.
On the solemn feasts and on the Sabbaths

we take such bodies as ye see, and abide here, praising our Maker. And as other spirits who are sent through the divers regions of the air and the earth, so may we speed also. Now hast thou with thy brethren been one year upon thy journey : and six years yet remain. Where this day thou dost keep the Easter feast, there shalt thou keep it throughout every year of thy pilgrimage, and thereafter shalt thou find the thing that thou hast set in thy heart, the land that was promised to the saints." And when the bird had spoken thus, it raised itself up from the prow, and took its flight to the rest.

And when the hour of evening drew on, then began all the birds that were on the tree to sing as with one voice, beating their wings and saying, " *Praise waiteth for thee, O Lord, in Sion : and unto thee shall the vow be performed.*" And they continued repeating that verse, for the space of one hour. It seemed to the brethren that the melody and the sound of the wings was like a lament that is sweetly sung. Then said St. Brendan to the brethren, " Do ye refresh your bodies, for this day have your souls been filled with the heavenly bread." And when the feast was ended, the brethren began to sing the office : and thereafter they rested in quiet until the third watch of the night. Then the man of God awaking, began to rouse the brethren for the Vigils of the Holy Night. And when he had begun the verse, " *Lord, open thou my lips, and my heart shall show forth thy praise,*" all the birds rang out with voice and wing, singing " *Praise the Lord, all ye his angels : praise ye him, all his hosts.*" And even as at vespers, they sang for the space of one hour. Then, when dawn brought the ending of the night, they all began to sing, " *And let the beauty of the Lord our God be upon us,*" with equal melody and length of chanting, as had been at Matins. At Tierce they sang this verse : " *Sing praises to God, sing praises : sing praises unto our King, sing praises: sing ye praises with understanding.*" And at Sext they sang, " *Lord, lift up the light of thy countenance upon us, and have mercy upon us.*" At Nones they said, " *Behold how good and how pleasant it is for brethren to dwell together in unity.*" And so day and night the birds sang praises to God. And throughout the octaves of the Feast they continued in the praises of God. . . .

118

Here then the brethren remained until the Whitsun Feast : for the sweet singing of the birds was their delight and their reviving. . . . But when the octave of the Feast was ended, the Saint bade his brethren to make ready the ship, and fill their vessels with water from the spring. And when all was made ready, came the aforesaid bird in swift flight, and rested on the prow of the ship, and said, as if to comfort them against the perils of the sea : " Know that where ye held the Lord's Supper, in the year that is past, there in like fashion shall ye be on that same night this year. . . . And after eight months ye shall find an island . . . whereon ye shall celebrate the Lord's Nativity." And when the bird had foretold these things, it returned to its own place.

Then the brethren began to spread their sails and go out to sea. And the birds were singing as with one voice, saying, " *Hear us, O God of our salvation, who art the confidence of all the ends of the earth, and of them that are afar off upon the sea.*" And so for three months they were borne on the breadth of ocean, and saw nothing beyond sea and sky.

ST. CAINNIC AND THE MICE

ONE Sunday St. Cainnic was lodged on the island of Inish Ubdain: but the mice of that place gnawed his shoes and nibbled them and ate them. And the holy man, when he was aware of their naughtiness, cursed the mice, and cast them out of that island for ever. For all the mice, assembling in a body, according to the word of St. Cainnic, precipitated themselves into the depths of the sea, and mice on that island have not been seen unto this day.

ST. CAINNIC AND THE SEA-BIRDS

ANOTHER time St. Cainnic was lodged one Sunday on another island, called En inish, the Isle of Birds. But the birds on it were garrulous and extremely loquacious, and gave annoyance to the Saint of God. So he rebuked their loquacity, and they obeyed his command, for all the birds got together and set their breasts against the ground, and held their peace, and until the hour of matins on Monday morning they stayed without a movement and without a sound, until the Saint released them by his word.

ST. CAINNIC AND THE STAG

ANOTHER time when St. Cainnic was in hidden retreat in solitude, a stag came to him, and would hold the book steady on his antlers as the saint read on. But one day, startled by a sudden fear, he dashed into flight without the abbot's leave, carrying the book still open on his antlers: but thereafter, like a fugitive monk to his abbot, the book safe and unharmed still open on his antlers, he returned.

ST. KEVIN AND THE COW

WANDERING by himself through lonely places, the blessed Kevin came one day upon a glen set in a hollow of the hills and lovely with running water. For there were two lakes, and clear streams here and there flowing down from the mountains. And he went up the valley to the head of the glen where it narrows; there is a lake there, and the mountains very high above it; it lies at their feet, and they rise from its very verge. This valley used to be called in the Irish Glen De, but now it is called Glen da Lough, that is the glen of the two lakes. And St. Kevin settled himself beside the lake in a hollow tree and lived in these strait quarters for some while. Now and then he would go out to gather a few herbs and eat them, and drink a little water. And so he lived, for many days.

Now a herd from a neighbouring farm (the master's name was Bi), would some days bring his cows to pasture in this valley, where St. Kevin lived a hermit. And God, being minded to show his servant Kevin to men, made a cow

from that herd come daily to St. Kevin in his hollow: and it would lick the saint's clothes. And towards evening when she would hear the lowing of the herd returning, sated with green grass and well watered, and the high shouting of the herdsmen driving their beasts, she would hurry to the front of the herd, content with her own pasture. And every day as the herd made its way from the lap of the mountain into the valley, that cow would steal away from the rest, and come to the man of God. And every day she did as on the first day. And that cow had abundance of milk past belief, from the touch of the garments of the man of God. And the byremen, marvelling at the rich streams of milk from her, spoke of it to the master. And he said to the herdsman, " Do you know what has come to that cow? " The herd knew nothing of it, and his master said, " Keep a close eye on her, and see where she gets her good favour from."

So the next day the herdsman left his charge to the youngsters and himself followed after the cow, wherever she went. And the cow took her wonted track to the hollow tree, in which St. Kevin lived. And the herd, finding her licking the saint's coat, stood agape:

and then he fell to threatening the cow, and miscalling the man of God as a countryman might. And the saint was ill-pleased, for he feared that the man would betray his presence there. And then the herdsman drove the beasts home to the byre. But when they had got to the farm, the cows and calves fell into such a frenzy that the mothers did not know their own calves and would have killed them. The herdsman, terrified, told his master what he had seen in the valley, and at his bidding, came straight back to St. Kevin, and fell on his knees and begged God's saint to grant him his forgiveness. The saint adjured him, and he vowed not to betray him: for St. Kevin did not know that the story was already told. The man had his pardon, and was given holy water: and when he sprinkled it on the cows and calves, they recognized one another with the old love between them, and were tame again on the spot. But the fame of St. Kevin was carried over the whole countryside. And it came to the ears of some of the older saints, Eogan and Lochan and Enna, that St. Kevin was in that deserted valley: and they took him away with them, against his will, to his monastery. . . .

126

ST. KEVIN AND THE WILD BOAR

. . . . And in the end St. Kevin came back to his own country, and began to live in that lonely spot, in the glen of the two lakes, where he had been a hermit in his youth, and where the cow used to come to him, as has been told. For that lonely place had been dear to the blessed Kevin from the beginning. In the lower part of the valley he founded a great monastery, at the meeting of two clear rivers. And many came to him from here and there, and St. Kevin made them monks in that place. . . . Then St. Kevin commended his monastery to trusty men, and gave to each monk his charge. And himself went out from there alone to the head of the glen, as it might be a mile from the monastery, and built himself a tiny hut in a narrow strip between the mountain and the lake, where the trees grew close and there were clear brooks. And he forbade his monks to bring him food of any kind, nor any to come near him unless for great cause. . . . And the wild things of the mountains and the woods came and kept him

company, and would drink water, like domestic creatures, from his hands. . . .

After seven years, St. Kevin built himself a little oratory of osiers, on the northern margin of the lake, where he might make his daily prayer to God. And there the saint lived, known of none, and fed on no human food, as we have said. But there came a day when the huntsman of the King of Leinster, Brandubh son of Eochaid, of the seed of Enna, who made a slaughter beyond numbering and sore destruction in a great war against the northern provinces of Ireland—and the same Brandubh had the kingship of many of the Kingdoms of Ireland, after killing Aed the son of Ainmire, King of Tara and Inishowen in battle—the huntsman came down after his hounds into the glen, following a boar: and the boar made into St. Kevin's oratory, but the hounds did not go in, but lay on their chests outside, before the gate. And there was St. Kevin praying under a tree, and a crowd of birds perched on his shoulders and his hands, and flitting about him, singing to the saint of God. The huntsman looked: and dumbfounded he took his way back with his hounds, and for the sake of the holy solitary's blessing, let the boar go free. He told the marvel that he had seen to the King and to all of them. And there were times that the boughs and the leaves of the trees would sing sweet songs to St. Kevin, that the melody of heaven might lighten his sore travail.

ST. KEVIN AND THE ROOKS OF GLENDALOUGH

COLMAN, son of Carbri, chief of the fourth of the men of northern Leinster, in his youth took to wife a woman of rank, but since their habits did in no way agree, sent her away, and took another in her place. Now the woman thus dismissed was wise and dangerous in magic arts, and being passionate against her husband, Colman the chief, she brought to death all the children of the other by her incantations ; for as soon as she heard that a son or a daughter had been born to him, she would come from wherever she was to stand over against the dun where the child lay, and sing magic songs, until the little creature was dead. So, when a little son was born to him in his old age, he was straightway baptised, lest he should die through her witchcraft unchristened ; and he was called Faoláin. And then the chief his father sent him to St. Kevin, that he might protect him by the strength of God from this woman, and bring him up in the

ways of the world. And he offered him to
St. Kevin, promising that he and his seed
after him should be buried by the house
of St. Kevin for ever, and should serve him,
if Faoláin should escape alive. And St.
Kevin took the child gladly, and brought
him up as a layman should be, even as his
father had said ; and he loved him dearly.
But St. Kevin knew not where to look for
new milk to feed the small babe, because
women and cows were far from his monastery : and he prayed to God to give him
some assistance in the matter. And God
sent St. Kevin a doe from the mountain
near by, and on her milk the baby Faoláin
was reared. Twice a day until the child
was grown, the doe would come to St.
Kevin's monastery, and there be milked by
one of the brethren, and go back in all
gentleness to her pasture.

But there came a day when the brother,
milking her out of doors, set down the
vessel with the milk on the ground : and
up came a greedy rook intent upon a drink,
and with its beak upset both pail and milk
on the ground. And seeing it, St. Kevin
spoke to that rook. "For long enough,"

132

said he, "shalt thou and thy race do penance for this crime. For on the day of my departure to heaven, there shall be much preparing of beef, and ye shall not eat thereof. And if any one of you make so bold as to touch so much as the blood or the offal of the cattle that shall be slain during those days, he shall die on the spot. And everywhere shall be merrymaking, but ye on the heights of these mountains that stand round us shall be sad, cawing and having the law of one another for very dismalness." And this marvel is fulfilled every year unto this day, even as the Saint foretold.

THE MOUNTAINS THAT ARE
CREATURES OF GOD

AFTER these things the Angel of God came to St. Kevin, saying, "O saint of God, God hath sent me to thee, to bring thee to the place which the Lord hath appointed thee, to the east of the lesser lake, and there thou shalt be with thy brethren : for in that place shall thy resurrection be."

Saint Kevin said, "If it had not displeased my Lord, in this place where I have borne travail for Christ, I would fain have remained until my death."

Then answered the Angel, "If thou wilt go with thy monks to this place, there shall be many of the sons of life in it until the end of the world, and when thou art gone thy monks shall have a sufficiency of this world's goods. And many thousands of blessed souls shall rise with thee from that place, to the kingdom of Heaven."

Said St. Kevin, " Indeed, O holy messenger, it is not possible for monks to dwell in that valley hemmed in by the mountains, unless God should aid them by His power."

Then answered the Angel, " Hear these words, O man of God. Fifty men of thy monks if thou wilt have it so shall God fill with heavenly bread, and naught of earthly sustenance at all, if they remain of one spirit in Christ after thy death : and to each of them that dies shall another succeed in the fear and the love of God, in habit and in vow, until the Day of Judgment."

Said St. Kevin, "I like it not that there should be so few monks after me in that place."

Then answered the Angel, " If thou likest it not that there should be so few in that place, then shall many thousands live there, without stint or poverty, God supplying their worldly store, for ever. And thou from thy heavenly seat shalt rule thy family on earth, even as thou wilt, in Christ. And by God's aid, thou shalt rule thy monks here and hereafter. For this place shall be holy and revered : the kings and the great ones of Ireland shall make it glorious to the glory of God because of thee, in lands, in silver and in gold, in precious stones and silken raiment, in treasures from over sea, and the delights of kings, and rich shall be its harvest fields. A great city shall rise there. And the burial place of thy monks shall be most sacred, and none that lie beneath its soil shall know the pains of hell. And verily if thou shouldst will that these four mountains which close this valley in should be levelled into rich and gentle meadow lands, beyond question thy God will do it for thee."

Said St. Kevin, " I have no wish that the creatures of God should be moved because of me : my God can help that place in some other fashion. And moreover, all the wild creatures on these mountains are my house mates, gentle and familiar with me, and they would be sad of this that thou hast said." And in such discourse the Angel of God and St. Kevin made their way across the waters of the lake.

ST. KEVIN AND THE BLACKBIRD

AT one Lenten season, St. Kevin, as was his way, fled from the company of men to a certain solitude, and in a little hut that did but keep out the sun and the rain, gave himself earnestly to reading and to prayer, and his leisure to contemplation alone. And as he knelt in his accustomed fashion, with his hand outstretched through the window and lifted up to heaven, a blackbird settled on it, and busying herself as in her nest, laid in it an egg. And so moved was the saint that in all patience and gentleness he remained, neither closing nor withdrawing his hand: but until the young ones were fully hatched he held it out unwearied, shaping it for the purpose. And for a sign of perpetual remembrance of this thing, all the images of St. Kevin throughout Ireland show a blackbird in his outstretched hand.

ST. CIARAN OF CLONMACNOISE AND THE STAG

THE glorious and most saintly abbot Ciaran . . . had his origin from the northern part of Ireland, from the folk of the Ards. . . . He was like a burning lamp, of charity so rare that not only did the fervour and devotion of his pitiful heart go out to the relieving of the hunger of men, but he showed himself tireless in caring for the dumb beasts in their necessity. . . .

Then the blessed Ciaran went out from St. Senan and came to his brethren Luchen and Odran, living in the monastery which is called Isel, that is, the low-lying place : and for a while he lived with them. And his brothers made St. Ciaran their almoner and master of the guest house. Luchen, who was the elder, was abbot of that place, and Odran prior. And at one time, St. Ciaran was reading out of doors in the graveyard in the sun, when he suddenly spied some weary travellers going into the guest house : and hurriedly getting up, he forgot his book, and it lay open out of doors until

138

the morrow. Meantime, as he busied himself settling his guests in their quarters and bathing their feet and eagerly tending them, the night fell. In that same night there fell great rains : but by God's will the open book was found dry and sound : not a drop of rain had fallen upon it, and all the ground round about it was damp. For which St. Ciaran and his brethren gave Christ praise. . . .

One day, when St. Ciaran was working in the field, there came to him a poor man asking for alms. At that very hour a chariot with two horses had been brought in offering to St. Ciaran by a certain lord, the son of Crimthann, King of Connaught : and these horses and chariot gave Ciaran to this poor man. Now St. Ciaran's brothers could not endure the vastness of his charity, for every day he divided their substance among the poor, and so they said to him, " Brother, depart from us : for we cannot live in the same place with thee and feed and keep our brethren for God, because of thy un-bounded lavishness." To whom St. Ciaran made reply : " If I had remained in this place, it would not have been Isel (that is, the low-lying) : not low but high, but great and honour-able." And with that St. Ciaran blessed his

brothers, and taking his wallet with his books
on his shoulder, he set out from thence. And
when he had gone a little way from the place,
there met him on the path a stag, awaiting him
in all gentleness : and St. Ciaran set his wallet
on his back, and wherever the stag went, the
blessed Ciaran followed him. And the stag came
to Lough Ree, which is in the east of Connaught,
and stood over against Hare Island, which is
in that lake. Then St. Ciaran knew that God
had called him to that island : and blessing the
stag, he sent him away, and went to that island and dwelt there. And the fame of his
holiness spread abroad, and from far and near
good men came together to him, and St. Ciaran
made them his monks. . . .

And one day as they rowed across, St.
Ciaran's gospel which a brother was holding
carelessly fell into the lake, and for a great
while it lay under the waters and was not found.
But one summer day the cows came into the
lake, to cool themselves in the water from the
great heat of the sun : and when they were
coming out from it, the leather wallet in which
the Gospel had been put had caught about the
foot of one of the cows, and so the cow dragged
the wallet with her back to dry land : and

inside the sodden leather the book of the gospel was found, clean and dry and shining white, with no trace of damp, as if it had been hidden in a library. For which St. Ciaran rejoiced, and his brethren with him. . . .

And after these things came a man of Munster . . . Donnan by name, to St. Ciaran dwelling on Hare Island. And to him one day St. Ciaran said, " What seek you, my father, in these parts? " And St. Donnan replied, " Master, I seek a place to abide in, where I may serve Christ in exile." Then said St. Ciaran, " Abide, father, in this place: for I shall go to some other : I know that this is not the place of my resurrection." Then St. Ciaran gave Hare Island with his household goods to St. Donnan, and came to a place called Ard Mantain on the river Shannon : but he would not dwell in that place, and said, " I will not to dwell in this place, for here there will be a great plenty of the things of this world, and worldly delight : and hard would it be for the souls of my disciples to go to heaven, if I should live here : for the place belongs to the men of this world." And thereafter St. Ciaran left that place and came to the place which was called of old Ard Tiprat, but is now called Clonmacnoise. And coming to the place he said: "Here shall I dwell: for many souls shall go forth from this place to the Kingdom of God: and in this place shall my resurrection be." So there the blessed Ciaran lived with his disciples, and began to found a great monastery there: and many from all sides came to him, and his parish spread about him far: and the name of St. Ciaran was famous throughout all Ireland. And a famous and holy city rose in that place to the honour of St. Ciaran, and its name was Clonmacnoise . . . and in it whether they be kings or princes, the chiefs of the sons of Niall and of Connaught are buried beside St. Ciaran there. . . .

So for one year did our most holy patron saint Ciaran dwell in his city of Clonmacnoise. And when he knew that the day of his death was drawing nigh, he prophesied weeping of the future evils that would fall after his day upon that place: and said that their life would be a poor thing. Then said the brethren: "Father, what shall we do in the day of these calamities? Shall we abide here beside thy relics? Or shall we seek another place?" To whom St. Ciaran said: "Haste ye to some other place of peace, and leave my relics as it might be the dry bones of a stag on the mountain. Better for you that your life should be with my spirit in heaven, than that ye should abide dishonoured beside my bones upon earth." And when the hour of his departing drew nigh he bade them carry him out of doors from the house, and gazing up at the sky said, " Steep is that road : and it must needs be." The brethren said to him, " Father, we know that nothing is hard for thee: but for us feeble folk, there is sore dread in this hour." And again brought back into the house he lifted up his hand and blessed his people and his clergy, and having received the sacrifice of the Lord, on the ninth day of September he gave up the ghost, in the thirty-third year of his age.

ST. COLMAN AND THE COCK, THE MOUSE, AND THE FLY

NOW, among the other virtues with which the Holy Ghost had endowed him, he was a great lover and keeper of evangelic poverty, and so marvellous a despiser of transitory things, that he would have no earthly possessions, nor gifts, nor kept any property of his own at all, unless you could call property three small creatures that Ketinus saith he had in friendliness about him, a Cock, a Mouse, and a Fly. The way that he used the Cock was that its crowing wakened him at night to Lauds, as a bell might. But the offices rendered by the Mouse and the Fly were the stranger and more remarkable in that these whom nature has designed to the fret and annoyance of mankind, the amazing kindness of God directed, against the weight of nature, to tendance upon His servants. For this was the service of the Mouse to the man of God, that it would not allow him to sleep or lie at peace beyond the fixed hour that he had laid down for himself in his holy vows: but when his body and his tired limbs, worn

L

out with vigil and prayer and his other
austerities, would have craved sleep and rest
beyond the stern limits of his vow, the Mouse,
sometimes by gnawing at his clothes, sometimes by nibbling at his ear, would drag him
from all quiet. Dear was this office to the man
of God, for by it he saw not only his vows
fulfilled, but himself provoked by a dumb
creature to the service of God.

Yet scarcely less remarkable was the office
of the Fly. For when the man of God had
leisure to read his holy books, the Fly would
trot up and down his codex: and should some
one call him, or he had to go about other business, he would instruct the Fly to sit down
upon the line at which he had halted, and keep
his place until he should return to continue
his interrupted reading: which the Fly in-
fallibly would do. Marvellous are these condescensions of the grace of God, and, as one
might say, the collusions of Christ with His
saints: yet incredible only to those who have
too little thought for how marvellous is God in
His praises, how gracious and tender His
affection for those that sincerely love Him:
and how befitting His ineffable loving kindness
that those who have renounced all fellowship

and service of men that their spirits may be swifter to serve Him, should themselves receive the good offices of dumb beasts, and a kind of human ministering: and the God whose high and tremendous majesty they acknowledge and adore should yet be found by them a benign and most indulgent friend.

And yet it befell, in the ruling of that divine wisdom that in strange vicissitude now takes its favours from the servants of God and now bestows them, now will have them comforted, and now left desolate: it befell, as the aforesaid Ketinus relates, that these three little creatures died, and their kind service and company was lost to the man of God. And in heavy sorrow, he wrote of his loss to the friend of his spirit, St. Columba, Abbot of Iona, at that time living in austerity, far from his own land. And the story goes that in reply St. Columba wrote at once in jest and in wisdom, that " there is neither lack nor loss where neither substance nor property is found ": as though to question why a man of God, consecrated to supreme renunciation and to poverty, should set that heart on small things, which had renounced and spurned great things and high.

SOURCES

The Desert Fathers.

Pp. 3-7.   The Hermit's Garden : The Penitent Wolf :
Sulpicius Severus, *Dialogus*, I. c. 13, 14. (*Corp.
Script. Eccl. Lat.*)

P. 8.   The Blessed Ammon : Rufinus, *Historia Monachorum*, c. 8. (Migne, *P.L.* XXI. c. 420-1.)

P. 13.   St. Macarius and the Hyæna : from a French
translation of the Coptic text by Amélineau,
Monastères de la Basse-Egypte, 233 ff.

P. 17.   St. Pachome and the Crocodiles : *Vita S.
Pachomii* (translated by Dionysius Exiguus),
c. 17, 19. (Migne, *P.L.* LXXIII. c. 240 ff.)

P. 19.   The Abbot Helenus and the Wild Ass : Rufinus,
op. cit. c. 11.

P. 20.   The Abbot Helenus and the Crocodile : Palladius, *Historia Lausiaca*, c. 59. (Migne, *P.L.*
LXXIII. c. 1167.)

P. 22.   St. Simeon Stylites : *Vita* by Antonius his
disciple, c. X. (Migne, *P.L.* LXXIII. c. 330.)

P. 24.   The Unsociable Lion : *Verba Seniorum* (translated from the Greek of an unknown author by
John the Subdeacon in the sixth century), II.
c. 15. (Migne, *P.L.* LXXIII. c. 1003.)

P. 25.   The Abbot Gerasimus and the Lion : John
Moschus, *Pratum Spirituale*, c. 107. (Migne,
P.L. LXXIV. c. 172 ff.)

P. 30.   St. Jerome and the Lion and the Donkey :
Vita Divi Hieronymi. (Migne, *P.L.* XXII.
c. 209 ff.)

149

The Saints of the West.

P. 41. The Death of King Teudiric : *Book of Llan Dâv* (edited by J. G. Evans and J. Rhys), p. 141.

P. 44. St. Columba and the Crane : Adamnan, *Vita S. Columbae* (ed. J. T. Fowler), I. c. 48.

P. 46. St. Columba and the White Horse : *op. cit.* III. c. 23.

P. 50. St. Columban in the Vosges : Jonas, *Vita S. Columbani*, c. 15, 30. (Migne, *P.L.* LXXXVII. c. 1020, 1028.)

Pp. 53-55. St. Malo and the Sow : St. Malo and the Wren : Sigebert of Gembloux, *Vita S. Maclovii*, c. 14, 15. (Migne, *P.L.* CLX. c. 738 ff.)

Pp. 56-67. St. Cuthbert : Bede, *De Vita et Miraculis S. Cudberti*, c. 5 ; 9, 10 ; 17, 19, 20. (*Pat. Ecc. Ang. Bede, IV.*)

P. 68. St. Werburga and the Wild Geese : William of Malmesbury, *Gesta Pontificum*, IV. 172. (*Chronicles and Memorials.*)

P. 71. St. Benno and the Frog : *Vita* by Emser, c. 54, *Acta Sanctorum, Jun.* 16. (IV. 139.)

Pp. 73-91. *St. Godric.* The first paragraph of reminiscence, the bears, the hare, and the hunted stag, are from the *Vita* by Geoffrey, monk of Durham, *Acta Sanctorum*, Mai. 21. The remainder is from the more ornate *Libellus de Vita. . . . S. Godrici*, by his contemporary Reginald, also of Durham (Surtees Society) : cap. 22, 51, 52, 39, 71.

P. 93. St. Cuthbert's Birds and Bartholomew : from the *Vita* by Geoffrey, c. 24, 25, in the appendix to the *Historia Dunelmensis Ecclesiae* by Symeon of Durham. (*Chronicles and Memorials.*)

SOURCES

The Saints in Ireland.

The texts will be found in Plummer's *Vitae Sanctorum Hiberniae* (Oxford, 1910), under the titles of the various saints. *St. Brendan and the Sea Monsters* is from the *Vita Secunda* in the Appendix to Vol. II.

P. 137.   St. Kevin and the Blackbird: Giraldus Cambrensis, *Topographia Hibernica*, II. 28. (*Opera*, ed. Brewer, v. 116.)

P. 145.   St. Colman and the Cock, the Mouse, and the Fly: Colgan, *Vitae Sanctorum . . . Hiberniae*, I. 244a.